MANAGING PRESSURE AT WORK

Helen Froggatt and Paul Stamp

BBC BOOKS

Published by BBC Books
a division of BBC Enterprises Limited,
Woodlands, 80 Wood Lane, London W12 0TT

First published 1991

ISBN 0 563 36159 X

Set by Pye Campbell Communication Projects
The Elms, Tillington, Hereford HR4 8LN.

Printed and bound in England
by Clays Ltd, St Ives Plc
Cover printed
by Clays Ltd, St Ives Plc

Contents

Introduction

This is a book about pressure – a wonderful commodity! It harnesses many thousands of years of evolutionary development, and provides everyone with the opportunity of achieving their realistic, optimum performance - not just once, but over and over again – and to do so in good health. Pressure is the spice of life, but to use it wisely, we must realise that there are pitfalls to avoid in the trials and tribulations of modern-day living.

It is written particularly for the business community. Businessmen and women are especially vulnerable to the negative effects of pressure; as things happen fast in today's worrying environment, you can easily forget how you feel emotionally and physically. This can lead to a decline into physical health problems, inefficiency at the office, and deteriorating relationships. The cost of badly managed pressure is high; resulting in key personnel 'burn out', poor public image and lack of effective work.

This book forms part of an individual's approach to solving many of these problems. We decided to write on pressure management as we had a unique approach to the physical effects of pressure. Even before we specialised in stress management, our osteopathic practice brought us in touch with many people who had stress-related problems, and it was our observation that most people ran into problems with their backs due either to a lack of awareness or a blocking out of the signals of pain and discomfort that their body was sending them.

This led us to formulate a message which we consider fundamental to pressure management. To be able to manage a situation effectively you have first to understand it by being aware of it and what it is doing to you. Remember that we create stress for ourselves.

Awareness is therefore fundamental to effective pressure management.

More emphasis is often placed on the end product, rather than how to achieve that end product. Physical effort where none is necessary, breath-holding and mental anxiety can all be side effects of trying too **hard** to achieve something which is probably actually quite easy to do.

In the relaxation and awareness sections of the book, we suggest that not only is relaxation necessary for rest and revitalisation but it can also be a feature of how you work towards your goals and how you move in your daily activities.

Section 1:
Understanding Stress

Checklist

☐ What is the relevance of stress in the 1990s?

☐ What is stress?

☐ What are the effects of stress?

☐ How do we get caught up on the stress wheel?

Stress and the 1990s

In these days of satellites, car facsimile machines and twenty-four-hour stock-markets, the only factor slowing things down is in fact man himself. The demands placed upon directors and, in turn, their managers in terms of productivity and quality control have never been so great. No wonder that 'stress' is a topical issue, with everyone asking what it is. Is it a reality and what are its costs to the country, the company, the individual? In fact it is a reality that has been with us since time began but due to changing lifestyles, technological advances and increasingly greater expectations, stress is now becoming a negative rather than a positive phenomenon.

As managers, how are you going to recognise when you are either 'stressed' or simply 'under pressure' - a condition which you have always felt actually enhances your performance at work? When you are able to answer this question you will be aware of how your own health is affected and you will also begin to identify those of your workforce who are suffering from stress and its effects. When a well-trained and valuable member of your workforce suddenly starts taking days off sick, are you just going to let him go after a couple of warnings or are you going to find out what has brought about this change? In the 1990s you must consider such a valuable resource carefully.

The sooner we all start talking about and recognising stress as a reality that can cost money, the sooner we can make the necessary adjustments to our managerial style, work environments and relationships in order to combat its effects.

Every telephone call or meeting, a difficult boss or awkward staff, may all contribute to the pressures of the day. Driving faster cars, travelling greater distances, traffic, pollution, overcrowding, government red tape – all can lead to high absenteeism, industrial accidents and litigation.

■ What is stress?

Do I know:

- What the fright, fight or flight response is?

- Why this is inappropriate in today's society?

- How this response manifests itself?

- The difference between **pressure** and **stress**?

- When stress is useful?

The stress response

The evolutionary emphasis of mankind has been to adapt and survive in a hostile environment, from the caveman fighting off predators to modern man driving on the M25. To this end, man has developed a nervous system which responds powerfully to any perceived threat or danger. This response is called the **fright, fight or flight mechanism**. It prepares the body to cope with any threat or danger either by 'fighting' it or running away and necessary biochemical changes occur to gear the body for the appropriate action.

When the brain perceives that you can cope, the mechanism has effectively provided a beneficial service thus increasing your ability to perform both physically and mentally. However, when the challenge is increased to a point where the brain perceives you **cannot** cope, despite your increased responses, it fails to help you deal with the threat and you may then be rendered useless.

The mechanism works by affecting many functions of the body via the autonomic nervous system.

The senses become more acute: pupils dilate, improving vision and so spotting danger. Smell and hearing also become more keenly tuned. Body awareness is heightened.

The heart-rate increases to pump blood round to supply muscles and allow them to work in either fighting or running away. A simultaneous rise in blood pressure aids circulation.

Blood flow is diverted from gut and kidney to muscles; the cessation of digestive processes can cause stomach pains. Blood flow is lost from skin resulting in pale complexion.

Clotting time is reduced to prepare for injury and minimise bleeding.

Red blood cells are produced, thus making transport for oxygen to the muscles more available.

Airways dilate and respiration is more rapid, increasing the available supply of oxygen.

Fat stores are mobilised to provide energy for muscles, accompanied by an increase in the release of glucose.

Hair stands on end to frighten the predator! **Teeth** are bared!

■ Today's society

When it was appropriate to have a physical response to the arousal mechanism, this was useful as a primitive means of survival. The caveman would stand his ground and fight or simply run away. However, there are few occasions these days when we are threatened by physical harm. Civilised man struggles to contain his nervous reactions. For example, should your boss provide new targets which appear totally unreasonable, do you punch him on the nose or run screaming from the office? When you are able to do neither, the effects of your stress response begin to work overtime on your body.

Many other things now trigger the stress response, from change to travel, or thoughts of the past or plans for the future. Little time is available either to adjust to change or recover from shock or grief. Diaries are full of appointments made weeks in advance, and at home partners have booked up the weekends.

We get into the habit of screwing down the lid on these instinctive reactions and maintaining acceptable social behaviour. Feelings are repressed and the sensations from your body denied. You no longer hear what your body is saying to you about its internal environmental condition.

As you proceed through this book you will see what effect this repression has and how you must develop the awareness to protect yourself and enjoy not only better health but possibly even a longer life.

Pressure or stress?

During the 1930s Hans Selye was responsible for much of the pioneering work which established the concept of 'stress'. The word stress was already in common usage, so he used 'enstress' to describe the positive types of stress and 'distress' to describe the negative types of stress.

Because stress has a negative connotation in most people's minds today we have chosen to use two terms to describe positive and negative reactions to stimulation.

Pressure is the term used for a reaction to a situation which you perceive you will be able to cope with successfully and which results in enthusiasm for new challenges, achievement and the happiness of good health.

Stress is the term used for a reaction to a situation which you perceive you will be unable to cope with successfully and which results in unwanted physical, mental or emotional deterioration.

If you look at the human function curve on the opposite page you will see how stimulation, pressure or stress affects efficiency according to the amounts experienced.

There are four main points to be noticed from this graph. First, that lack of stimulation or pressure does not enhance performance, so if you feel you are understimulated, think about taking on extra responsibilities or new challenges to improve your efficiency.

Secondly, it can be seen how the right amount of pressure has a positive effect on our lives, hence the old adage, if you want something done ask a busy person. Enough pressure enhances efficiency and enables goals to be achieved.

Thirdly, there is a point at which further pressure no longer has a beneficial effect on performance. As you approach your threshold it may only be a minor event which actually pushes you past your peak.

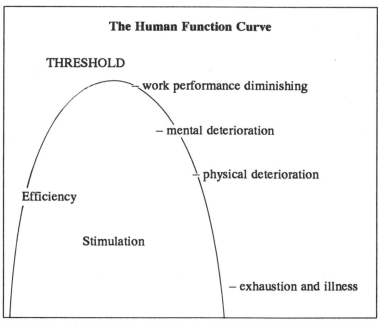

The Human Function Curve

THRESHOLD

work performance diminishing

– mental deterioration

– physical deterioration

Efficiency

Stimulation

– exhaustion and illness

You may have experienced this yourself when just one more interruption or hiccup in the day caused you intense frustration or anger – in other words the straw that broke the camel's back.

Fourthly, as the threshold is approached, if no attempt is made to rest and revitalise the body it goes into 'overdrive' in a vain attempt to sustain efficiency. The situation rapidly deteriorates; one no longer feels in control, it seems that there is a never-ending list of jobs to do and not enough time in which to complete them, time with the family is lost and the other long-term effects of sustained pressure begin to be experienced. Physical and mental health both suffer, leading to the exhaustion and ill health which not infrequently result in severe disability or death. The incidence of coronary heart disease (CHD) is currently higher in Britain than in any other European country and four times greater than in Japan, and a positive link has been shown between CHD and competitive, aggressive behaviour. CHD is more prevalent in men than in women; but an interesting American study revealed that working women with children were also more likely to develop CHD than those without. Sadly this is only one example of a stress-related illness. Indeed, it is estimated that 75 per cent of illnesses reported to GPs are in fact stress related.

As you look at the graph, picture which point on the curve you are at at the present moment. Do you need to increase the pressure in your life to improve your efficiency or do you need to slow down, take stock of your situation, cut out the unnecessary activities that are crammed into your life, realise your personal capacity and start saying 'No' to extra duties?

It may be that at this moment you are feeling well balanced with just the right amount of pressure to enable you to enjoy a rich and fulfilling life – that's great! But do you know why and how that is the case for you? By ensuring you understand how you have achieved this you should be able to maintain it even when crisis and change catch you off guard. Ask yourself several times a day 'what point am I at on the curve?' and you will find that it varies. You may also try this exercise in periods of weeks, months and years. A pattern of peaks and troughs should emerge.

Those who are company managers or employers must be able to identify how your workers are responding to pressure. Can you ensure they have enough to keep them interested in their work but not so much that they are overloaded and cannot cope? An example of the latter situation was a factory where the directors had asked their managers to increase productivity. This was passed on to the workforce by simply speeding up the machinery on the production line. Fortunately, an alert occupational health nurse wondered why, suddenly, so many workers off the floor were coming in to her suffering with headaches and pains. The problem was quickly identified and things soon returned to normal and there is no doubt that any potentially more serious industrial injuries which would have been far more costly to the company were avoided.

It is easy enough to see what went wrong there, but what about the individual members of your own workforce? How well do you relate to them? Do you know and understand them? People may get on fine at work as long as that is all they have to worry about, but when their lives are subjected to change from other sources they may quickly approach and pass their threshold. How will you know if this has happened? We will discuss this in later chapters but, for now, use the human function curve to make a form of quick assessment.

When is pressure useful?

Pressure is useful when the body is finely tuned in a way that enables us to achieve the best results and performance. For instance, a few nerves before an interview are often beneficial and result in an alertness and responsiveness that will impress the interviewer. The stimulation of this situation is, in fact, a positive pressure. However, too many nerves and a disastrous journey to the interview, leaving you short of time, may well mean that you exceed your threshold and are left feeling shaky and inarticulate.

The most spine-tingling performances of the opera singer are never given during rehearsals but when the house is packed, the lights are on and the curtain rises. Athletes only break records when there is the excitement of competition to stimulate them, not when quietly training at home. These achievements are the result of peaks in performance. It would not be possible to break Olympic records every day. The challenge is to find just the right amount of pressure under which to work efficiently and effectively with consistency, while saving a little in reserve to accommodate those slightly more pressurised situations and learning to rest and recover from them afterwards. To balance demands or 'threats' in your life against relaxation and pleasure will enable you to make the most of pressure.

When your mind and body are in harmony with one another, you are aware of your body, your environment, situations around you and how they are making you feel. Your breathing is relaxed, improving communications and erasing ambiguity. With clarity of thought, time and compatible body language, not only will you be understood but you will be open to receive any necessary information.

Checklist

☐ Be aware of the short-term effects stress has on your body

☐ Are you free of the long-term effects of stress?

☐ Does stress improve or inhibit your performance? Why?

☐ Does the mind and body principle apply to you?

☐ Are you 'in control' or caught up in the stress wheel?

☐ Do you notice who else around you is suffering from the effects of stress?

We've already seen how the primitive alarm response was designed to improve physical performance and mental alertness. When managing pressure on a day-to-day basis physical preparation is not used as much as the accompanying mental alertness. So even when coping well under pressure it is still important to make time for relaxation and physical activity in order to keep healthy.

Without this period of rebalancing relaxation and physical activity, the body chemicals that were released into the bloodstream associated with the alarm response are not entirely used up. In addition, the rich sources of energy in the form of fats and glucose will not be completely metabolised. Instead they all remain in the system and create an imbalance in the body's physiology as they build up and often begin destructive processes. What is more, if stimulation and demand continue, more body chemicals are produced which contribute to further imbalances. The base is thus created for the detrimental physical and mental effects of stress which may lead to disease.

So, what happens in the body when you experience pressure and what is it that makes you improve your performance? And, conversely, what happens to create that slightly panicky feeling when the situation is a bit stressful? By understanding something about body chemicals and the autonomic nervous system these processes really begin to make sense. You will then have a sound base from which to start using them best or, if necessary, to develop them by changing one or two aspects of your life.

If you've previously underestimated the long-term implications of stress, when you read in more detail how they develop and the insidious way in which they impinge on your life, we think you'll be more convinced and you will realise how stress has a price, not only to individuals, but also to the companies they work for.

The body chemicals associated with pressure and stress

The autonomic nervous system (ANS) is the caretaker of the body. It is involved in the everyday running and maintenance of the body, balancing vital body processes such as digestion, heart-rate and temperature control as conditions change. Throughout life this 'caretaker' is at work.

The two divisions of the ANS are the sympathetic nervous system (SNS) and the parasympathetic nervous system (PSNS) which complement and contrast one another, balancing the body's internal environment, by a process known as homoeostasis. The SNS results in energy being used up and is responsible for preparing the body for action and exercise, i.e. the expression of the alarm response. The main role of the PSNS is to ensure the conservation and build-up of energy stores. This allows the body the right climate in which to rest, relax and rejuvenate.

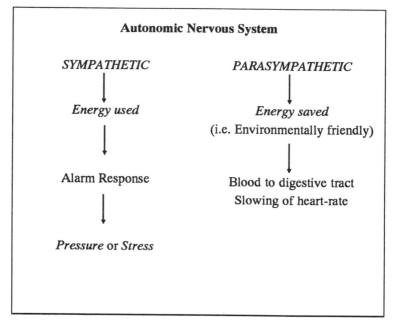

Autonomic Nervous System

SYMPATHETIC

↓

Energy used

↓

Alarm Response

↓

Pressure or *Stress*

PARASYMPATHETIC

↓

Energy saved
(i.e. Environmentally friendly)

↓

Blood to digestive tract
Slowing of heart-rate

The ANS is controlled by the brain. The senses relay information to the cerebral cortex where it is evaluated and passed down into the area of the brain responsible for emotions, called the limbic system. The force and intensity of the emotions associated with the situation can then be incorporated into this information. This is then transmitted to the hypothalamus which orchestrates the nervous and hormonal response to the perceived situation by either stimulating the SNS or PSNS and/or the pituitary gland.

Part of the response of the SNS is to produce two chemical messengers or hormones called noradrenalin and adrenalin. These chemical messengers are produced at nerve junctions in the short term and in the adrenal glands when arousal is experienced over a longer period.

Noradrenalin and adrenalin have some functions in common such as tensing the muscles ready for action, increasing the heart-rate, mobilising fats and glucose stores from the liver, and shunting blood from less important areas like the digestive tract to the muscles. Noradrenalin is associated particularly with sharpening the senses and intellect. Its effect on the body is not as dramatic as adrenalin.

Adrenalin is more dramatic in its effects on areas of the body associated with the 'flight' mechanism of the alarm response.

If the body is subjected to continuous stimulation, i.e. stress, another set of chemicals is produced in an attempt to maintain performance. These are the steroid hormones of the pituitary gland and adrenal cortex. Cortisol is the more significant hormone and it has a wide range of powerful effects. Principally, it works to keep high levels of fats and sugars, i.e. sources of energy, in the bloodstream and to suppress the immune system.

Conversely, the level of sex hormones produced by the adrenal cortex is lowered, impairing libido and fertility.

The chemical messenger of the PSNS is acetylcholine. This promotes muscle relaxation, slowing of the heart-rate, lowering of the blood pressure, and a general rebalancing of the body's physiology and replenishing of the chemical stores.

It is the balance of SNS and PSNS which helps maintain a healthy person. If the SNS is continually stimulated, the restorative effects of the PSNS do not have the opportunity to rebalance the body and so stress-related illness results.

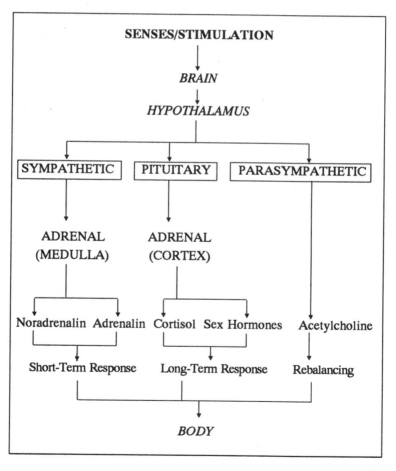

Checklist

When I have a busy day, do I:

☐ Feel pleasure or distress?

☐ Feel alertness or confusion?

☐ Experience success or failure?

☐ Plan my time well or run out of time completely?

☐ Take part in good decision-making or have difficulty in decision-making?

☐ Express my thoughts clearly or keep my opinions to myself?

☐ Take longer to grasp an idea/situation or quickly grasp ideas/situations?

☐ Have relaxed breathing or rapid breathing and sighing?

☐ Have a comfortable posture or neck pain and shoulder stiffness?

■ The short-term effects of pressure and stress

The short-term effects of both pressure and stress are a result of the alarm response. The difference between them lies in one's perception of events and consequently the degree to which the response is activated. In a pressure situation, you feel you can cope and thus experience the beneficial effects of the alarm response. If, however, you perceive that you cannot cope, the adaptive resources of the body will be overloaded by the alarm response, resulting in an inability to perform effectively.

If the situation is of short duration and is followed by a period of mental and physical rebalancing involving the parasympathetic division of the ANS, then the effects of the pressure or stress will be limited to that time span.

■ *The joy of pressure*

When enjoying the effects of the alarm response in a pressure situation, you experience an alertness and clarity of thought due to the production of noradrenalin by the adrenal glands enabling you to make good decisions, communicate effectively and act confidently, thus ensuring success and satisfaction.

From the manifestations of the alarm response, we see how we breathe more deeply to ensure a good supply of oxygen to the muscles and brain. As well as facilitating brain activity, this helps to avoid muscle fatigue and maintain good posture.

Because the lines of communication between mind and body are open, you will be aware of your body's needs. As we have seen, following a period of SNS activity, as experienced in the pressure situation, we must take time to replenish energy stores via the parasympathetic system. If you wish to maintain the ability to respond to pressure and use it to enhance your work and social life, you must respect the needs of your body. As much dedication to resting, renourishing and revitalising your body should be made as to your work. By doing this you will be putting money in your bank of life.

■ *Was it just a bad day?*

When you reach a situation in which you feel swamped and unable to cope, your threshold on the human function curve has been reached and passed. The 'flight' mechanism of the alarm response involving the effects of adrenalin is in operation. Your body has been prepared to 'run away' but generally you don't or can't. An internal conflict is in progress creating feelings of anxiety and tension. You probably don't feel confident and will be unclear in your communications. Plans don't work and you're very short of time. Concentration is difficult, you lose awareness of your body and may experience co-ordination problems - bumping into people and furniture, and dropping things as you dash about in a generally ineffectual way.

On top of this, you may suffer the physical effects of stress - a pounding heart, indigestion, stomach cramps, sweaty palms and headaches which are all the work of adrenalin. By the end of the day you will have neck and shoulder stiffness and will be feeling absolutely shattered.

This may all have started as a result of one major event beyond your control, or you may have been enjoying a busy day when you were asked to squeeze just one more task in, or something minor went wrong which had many repercussions. The balance between an enjoyable pressure day and a stressful day is often a very delicate one. By observing and being aware of how this happens you begin to obtain control of the situation. This is discussed further later in the book.

If it's been a rough day, how are you going to recover? What does your body need? As you will have lost touch with your body during the stress of the day, it will be necessary to make a more concerted effort to allow the PSNS to operate.

The short-term effects

	PRESSURE	STRESS
E **M** **O** **T** **I** **O** **N** **A** **L**	Confident Efficient Pleasure Good self-image Assertive	Anxious Tense Distress Swamped Under-confident Poor self-image Depression
B **E** **H** **A** **V** **I** **O** **U** **R** **A** **L**	Good concentration Clarity of thought Awareness Effective planning Decisive Objectives achieved Clear communication Time to rest and relax	Poor Concentration Confusion Lack of awareness Poor planning Not completing tasks Ambiguous communication Lack of time Fatigue
P **H** **Y** **S** **I** **C** **A** **L**	Wellness Good posture Relaxed breathing Aware of body needs Vitality	Poor posture Rapid breathing Tight chest Indigestion/stomach cramps Shoulder and neck pain Headaches Pupils dilate Sweating/clammy feeling Low vitality

The long-term effects of stress

Checklist

How much stress do I have?

Emotional

- ☐ Most of the time I feel tense and wound up.
- ☐ I don't often laugh or feel happy.
- ☐ There is no one in my life to confide in.
- ☐ For some reason I am irritable and often angry.
- ☐ At times I feel tearful for no apparent reason.

Behavioural

- ☐ I used to be punctual but now I always seem to be late for appointments.
- ☐ My memory just isn't as good as it was.
- ☐ I don't seem to settle down and get on with things; there always seem to be distractions.
- ☐ My sex drive has diminished. I am impotent.
- ☐ I haven't got time to worry about how I look.
- ☐ Often, just one thing goes round and round in my head.

Physical

- ☐ At times I feel breathless.
- ☐ I get chest pains and pins and needles.
- ☐ My head aches and often feels tight.
- ☐ Coughs and colds plague me.
- ☐ My back has been playing up again.
- ☐ I seem to have a lot of indigestion and acid reflex these days.
- ☐ The doctor has given me pills for high blood pressure.
- ☐ It was frightening going to hospital - the doctor said I could have had a small heart attack.

The long-term effects of stress

So it was a lousy day yesterday. Well, actually it's been a busy . week, or even, when you think about it, a busy month! You may even find it's difficult to remember the last time you didn't feel tired or when you didn't have a long list of jobs to do. These continual demands have taken you past your 'threshold' on the human function curve. The coping resources of the body have become steadily eroded.

In an attempt to provide the energy to cope with demands, the effects of adrenalin and noradrenalin are backed up by the release of cortisol. The changes brought about explain the emotional, behavioural and physical changes that occur. There is no opportunity for recovery and the decline to ill health has begun.

■ *How does it feel?*

When you are tired it is usual to feel a bit depressed and dull, without any sparkle. Your fuse is short; you might be snappy and irritable, even becoming angry. Perhaps you won't feel as conscientious as usual. Some people find they are near to tears and cry either for no apparent reason or over a minor incident. You're certainly not at your best like this and it may be easier to withdraw a little, but you could then begin to feel isolated and paranoid. Though we are often severe in judging ourselves, these emotional responses to physical events in your body are not signs of weakness.

■ *How do you act?*

When you feel like this, it follows that there will be changes in your behaviour at work and socially. To shake off those feelings of being one step behind, or to get yourself going for the day, you may well have a cup of strong coffee. The effect of the caffeine becomes more and more short-lived, so the number of cups a day becomes more numerous. How many people do you know who have half-drunk cups of coffee around them and are always reaching for another? Then, to stop the shakes from all the coffee, the number of cigarettes increases. Some people prefer drugs. The young executives on the stock-market use many stimulants to keep going and some are 'burnt out' after a couple of years.

How and what we eat will often change under these circumstances - a gobbled take-away sandwich at lunchtime, and take-away food late at night. Some people indulge, overeat and gain weight, while others lose weight. Either way the need to refuel the body is not treated with respect.

For some people, it is simply how they organise their time that illustrates how their coping resources are gradually being challenged and that they are suffering from the long-term effects of stress. They may skip meal-breaks, work late and arrive early. Conversely, others will be repeatedly late, clock-watch and take long breaks.

A loss of libido, which may be accompanied by premature ejaculation or even impotence for men and failure or difficulty in reaching orgasm for women, is common when you are stressed for long periods. It may be that you're too tired to notice, but for some this may be extremely worrying. Less love-making and touching may undermine relationships and set up tension. The physical touching involved in caressing and foreplay brings pleasurable sensations and so increases our body awareness. This may be lost through the long-term effects of stress.

■ *What are the effects on your physical health?*
The prolonged effects of stress may lead to stress-related disease. The cardio-vascular, the digestive and the immune system are well-known areas where such disease develops. More recently, attention has been paid to the altered breathing pattern known as **hyperventilation,** and problems relating to posture and the musculo-skeletal system can also be included here. In our work as osteopaths we noticed that many people were experiencing stress in their lives when they came to the practice with musculo-skeletal injuries.

■ *Stress-related diseases of the cardio-vascular system*
Adrenalin and noradrenalin work to increase blood pressure by
increasing the heart-rate and constricting peripheral blood vessels. This
can cause damage to the smooth lining of the blood vessels, allowing
fatty plaques to build up, which narrow the diameter of the blood
vessel. The impaired blood flow may then cause cramp-like symptoms
in that area. If this happens to the heart, the pain caused is called
angina. The viscosity of the blood is increased, the spleen contracts and
releases red blood cells and platelets and the bone marrow is stimulated
to produce more red and white blood cells. In blood vessels already
damaged by hypertension and fatty plaques, blockages may develop. If
this occurs in the heart or brain then catastrophic effects such as strokes
and heart attacks may result.

Noradrenalin, adrenalin and cortisol produce higher levels of fats,
cholesterol and sugar in the bloodstream. It has been found that the
fatty plaques which build up in blood vessels are mainly composed of
cholesterol. Therefore, a high level of circulating blood cholesterol can
increase the risk of coronary heart disease, strokes, hypertension and
sudden cardiac death; the level of circulating blood cholesterol is
increased most noticeably in people suffering from high levels of stress.
(See pages 76 and 133 for other ways of reducing circulating cholesterol
levels.)

■ *Stress and the immune system*
In a chronic incessant stress situation, more cortisol is produced, impairing
the function of the immune system, thus making us vulnerable to even
minor illnesses such as colds or flu.

■ *Stress and the digestive system*
A rise in the level of circulating cortisol has dramatic effects on the
resistance of the lining of the digestive tract to its own acid, and can
cause ulcers. Adrenalin and noradrenalin close down the digestive tract
by diverting blood away from it, so if you try to eat while stressed, you
can experience such problems as indigestion, nausea and diarrhoea.

■ *Stress and other disorders*
Adult diabetes may commonly begin after a stressful period due to the extra strain put on the pancreas by high blood-sugar levels.

■ *Stress and breathing*
Breathing is essentially an unconscious activity. It performs two functions:

- an avenue of communication and expression of emotion;
- ventilation of the lungs to allow the exchange of carbon dioxide (CO_2) and oxygen (O_2) at a cellular level.

The passage of air through the vocal cords creates sound. This takes many forms, e.g. speech, laughter, screaming, crying or sobbing and may be expressed in many ways - joy, happiness, anger or fear, by varying volume, pitch and tone.

If we suppress this expression, we stop the passage of air. This means of control is therefore associated with 'holding' the breath. A tensing of the diaphragm and abdominal muscles is also commonly involved in this suppression.

You may well have experienced this suppression when shocked by bad news, when angry (count to ten!) or stunned to silence by fear. Left unexpressed, these feelings all contribute to our stress levels. This may occur in a moment or build up over the years.

Normal breathing patterns will be disrupted, forcing the respiratory effort to be made in the upper part of the rib-cage. This places strain on the muscles of the shoulder and neck and causes wear and tear and those familiar aches and pains.

When breathing correctly with the diaphragm, circulation and digestion are aided and support for the low back is provided. The heart, veins and abdominal organs are all massaged by the movement of the diaphragm when relaxed deep breathing occurs, so helping to protect against stress-related disease in these areas.

The low back is supported by the inflatable jacket of the abdomen which is pressurised by the descent of the diaphragm. When emotions become 'locked in' and the movement of the diaphragm is decreased, these valuable functions are impaired.

Added to this mechanical situation, adrenalin and noradrenalin also cause an increase in the respiratory rate and dilation of the airways in the lungs. Over a sustained period this can lead to overbreathing or hyperventilation. The 'buffer system' of the blood which maintains the correct PH (acid/alkalinity) is depleted by overbreathing, impairing the ability of the red blood cells to transport oxygen, and areas which have high metabolic rates (i.e. need loads of oxygen), such as the muscles and brain, are affected badly. This contributes to muscle fatigue, aches and pains and the confusion, mood swings, irritability, etc associated with stress. Other effects of hyperventilation include pins and needles, chest pain, visual disturbances and dizziness.

■ *Stress and posture*
Good posture is all about **balance** and **co-ordination**. When posture is balanced the workload on the muscles is considerably reduced because the weight of the body is taken through the bones. Co-ordination helps us to keep that balance when we are moving.

Stress, as we have seen already, leads to a lack of body awareness which allows us to adopt unbalanced positions for long periods of time. Have a look around the office - you will probably see people on the telephone, perched on chairs, or hunched over desks. Muscles that have been in a shortened position tighten, causing pain when changing position and contributing to poor posture. This imbalance through shortened muscles also predisposes the body to injury. Sadly, due to our sedentary lifestyles, this is now very common. Sitting at desks and VDU screens and driving long distances are very static postures leading to muscle shortening and tightening.

Emotions and feelings are not only reflected in how we breathe, but also in our posture and the use of the body. This can be easily seen in children when they jump for joy or cower and sulk when reprimanded. Next time you meet a friend, try predicting how they are feeling by looking at their posture before you actually speak to them.

The long-term effects

PHYSICAL	**Breathing:**
	- Hyperventilation (sighing)
	- Visual disturbance
	- Chest pain
	- Muscle fatigue
	Posture:
	- poor breathing
	- risk back injury
	- neck pain
	Awareness: T P + B
	- Indigestion - food
	- Developing ulcers
	Immune system: flu, arthritis
	Blood pressure: ageing
	- risk disease
	Weight gain/loss

EMOTIONAL	Denial
	Depression, Dull
	Anger and irritation
	Tearful - near surface
	Unhappiness
	Withdrawing from
	relationships
	Isolation
	Paranoia
	Lost ability to feel/care

BEHAVIOURAL	Tardiness
	Stimulants
	Long breaks
	Clock-watching
	Staying late
	Memory
	Insomnia
	Impotence
	Loss of libido
	Untidy appearance
	Comforts - food, money,
	treats

The stress-spiral

Once past 'threshold' the changes in mood, behaviour and health are initially disguised so we fail to recognise them. The **stress spiral** illustrates how the compensations made to maintain efficiency e.g. using stimulants, staying at work, replacing thought with effort, serve only to accelerate a further decline. We ultimately feel we are victims of circumstance caught in a 'whirlpool' of stress, unaware of how we came to be there. Many people attending stress courses have been sent by their doctors, partners or employers. The fact that they cannot see they are experiencing the effects of stress is not unusual. Looking at the stress-spiral it can be seen how events, feeling and health have an accelerating effect on one another without our realising it.

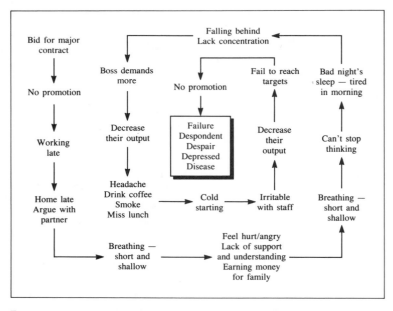

Draw your own stress-spiral to illustrate the knock-on effects of stress factors in your life. Include such things as routine events, new demands and changes, and how you feel/felt.

Checklist

☐ Is your mind the bread-winner?

☐ Do you take your body for granted?

☐ Is the body simply the service station and transport vehicle for the mind?

☐ Where is the service station for the body (hospital)?

☐ Are you aware of where your head is more than where your feet are?

The mind and body principle

How can you be unaware of developing muscle tension, or the beginnings of an ulcer or an increased respiratory rate? These things do happen in the body you are attached to after all.

The answer is simply because the amount of sensory information that can be processed by the brain is limited and not infinite. The warning signals arrive, but you just don't pay any attention to them because your mind is on other things. We are all familiar with the idea of distraction helping when in pain; after an operation, while playing cards or reading, pain seems OK, but as soon as we stop and try to go to sleep - back it comes... nag, nag, nag. Similarly, music played during exercise enables us to carry on a little longer or jog a bit further. These are considered useful forms of distraction. However, distraction and lack of awareness are at the very root of the development of stress-related disease.

Imagine this situation:

Suzanne left home just a bit late this morning and hit the rush-hour traffic which made her very late for work. She arrived to find the photocopying machine on her floor out of order, two men are off sick which meant she had to organise cover and the directors were waiting for her in the boardroom to look at the report she was frantically trying to photocopy. The report was copied but in the rush she knocked the papers off the table, mixing all the pages together, delaying her further. Suzanne probably had no idea how she was breathing, which muscles had tensed up, how her stomach felt and she probably experienced some eye-hand co-ordination difficulty. Suzanne had so many distractions that her body awareness was totally lost. We've all had similar experiences from time to time, which isn't too bad in isolation as long as a **serious** accident is not the outcome of such a whirlwind of events.

But imagine this type of situation occurring several times a day! When you arrive home feeling exhausted, is it any wonder? It is probably the first time you have noticed your body all day. Despite the fact that your headache was developing during the morning, your stomach churning and your hands sweating, you weren't aware of this until now. Is the body merely a transport unit for the brain and senses? Well no, it's not, but that is really the way we treat our bodies. By developing an awareness so that our minds and bodies are in unison we can protect ourselves against stress-related disease and begin the process of change.

Section 2:
INCREASING AWARENESS

Checklist

☐ How will awareness help me in business?

☐ Do I know why breathing has a part to play in pressure management?

☐ Do I consider my posture and body-use to be good?

☐ Do I include at least three simple relaxation and awareness routines in my day?

Increasing awareness: Coming to your senses

Being aware of your body can help prevent the build-up of tension and, therefore, prevent the damaging physical and mental effects of stress. Body awareness means having your attention in your body making sure mind and body are united. The resulting perception, co-ordinated body movements and appreciation of your inner feelings will help protect you and give you the confidence and vitality associated with positive pressure. You will enjoy a renewed receptiveness to the world around you.

Learning to use pressure without stress developing requires you to gain an insight and understanding of yourself and your life by putting prejudice to one side and observing with a quiet, open mind. But, because stress causes confusion and mental fatigue, you need to become more aware of your body so as to quieten the mind and allow this reawakening of the senses.

As you develop your sense of awareness, you will also enjoy other benefits. Instead of your mind becoming cluttered with daydreams or thoughts of the past or future, you will be firmly in the present, enjoying sharper concentration. As you stride through your day, a moment of beauty may be appreciated, a smile exchanged or a joke shared.

Finally, consider how this new awareness will translate to your business life. You won't easily be thrown off balance or disorientated and when recognising tension in others you will be able to choose whether you would make more progress if you helped them to relax or if it would be to your advantage to work with that tension and catch them off balance. When you are more aware, you are able to read and make the most of body language and non-verbal communications. Similarly, you may choose to **use** them yourself to be more clearly understood.

In order to develop this skill, we need to look at awareness and relaxation in terms of breathing and posture. Postural awareness is vital in preventing muscle tension and fatigue. It goes hand in hand with being in the present. Relaxation helps you to rebalance after encountering stressful situations by:

* relieving muscle tension and aches;
* quietening the mind;
* aiding sleep;
* making personal relationships more harmonious.

To develop these skills, your attention must monitor your body use. Like any other new art, body awareness exercises must be learned and practised. Initially they may seem difficult and time-consuming but with a little determination the benefits will be yours to enjoy in today's competitive business environment.

Breathing

Checklist

I know:

☐   how to use my diaphragm when breathing

☐   which are the muscles responsible for moving the ribs

☐   the support the diaphragm provides for my back

☐   when I use the upper part of my chest to breathe

☐   how good my chest looks in the mirror

☐   how my breathing pattern is affected by driving

☐   when my chest tightens up and I breathe quickly

☐   how relaxing it is to breathe deeply and rhythmically

☐   how posture and breathing relate to one another

I want to practise breathing and relaxation to make the most of
pressure in my life.

Breathing

Although breathing is mainly an unconscious activity, everyone exercises breath control in everyday life, e.g. when shouting, talking and singing. So there is a degree of conscious control as well. This can be used in relaxation techniques and also in developing a sense of body awareness. When you focus on your breathing your attention will be brought back to your body. Altered breathing patterns causing symptoms such as pins and needles and neck and shoulder stiffness are associated with stress. By re-establishing calm breathing patterns after stressful periods, you can help to relax your body once again and relieve such symptoms. Calm breathing patterns can also be used to prevent pressure situations from becoming stressful.

In learning breathing and relaxation techniques it is useful to understand some of the underlying anatomy. It is also important to become aware of how you breathe and the circumstances which alter how you breathe. Although it may seem difficult to include some of the following exercises into your daily routine, with time they will become habit.

First, to find the lower border of your rib-cage start at the front. Place your hands along the lower margin of the ribs with finger-tips meeting in the middle just below the breastbone. Explore this area by gently pushing inwards; the firmness of the ribs are easily distinguishable from the softness of the stomach.

Follow the line of the ribs down and out to the sides and then around to your back. The muscles of the back feel harder, giving you less contrast, so push more firmly to distinguish the line of the rib-cage. Visualise this shape from the front, the sides, behind and above. Draw it if you find it helpful.

Attached to the inside of these bony borders is the diaphragm - a dome-shaped sheet of muscle, acting as a flexible partition between the thorax and abdomen. It is anchored centrally by a circle of non-contractile tendinous tissue, at the periphery to the bony borders of the lowest ribs and at the back by two tendinous slips attaching to the front of the upper lumbar vertebrae.

The diaphragm is an important breathing muscle. However, because it is pierced by three major structures, i.e. the oesophagus, the vena cava and the aorta, it is also used in circulation and digestion. The tone of the diaphragm helps prevent the reflux of acidic gastric juices from the stomach into the oesophagus (heartburn). The movement of the muscle has a beneficial effect on blood returning to the heart from the legs, abdomen and pelvis via the vena cava. It is the massaging effect and change of pressure created in the abdomen and pelvis which helps this.

In addition, the diaphragm helps support the low back, not only due to its attachments to the upper vertebrae but also by its action. As it flattens and contracts, the pressure in the abdomen increases and the combined effect with the abdominal muscles is like an inflatable, supportive jacket supporting the low back. When weightlifters strut up and down breathing deeply, it is not all showmanship - they're actually using these muscles!

As the diaphragm contracts and flattens and makes the volume of the thorax greater, air is drawn into the lungs. The volume is also enlarged by the action of the scalene muscles which lift the upper ribs and breastbone forwards and upwards and the intercostal muscles which govern the movement of the lower ribs outwards. The scalene muscles attach to the upper vertebrae in the neck and down and forwards on to the first three ribs. The intercostals, as their name suggests, are attached between each rib.

The gentle, rhythmic motion of breathing should encompass both the movement of the diaphragm and the whole of the rib-cage.

Finding out how you breathe

Take time to discover how you breathe; it may be that you have never given this unconscious activity a second thought and may well find it difficult initially. Follow the procedure below to discover your own breathing pattern.

Place your hands, one below the other, on your breastbone. Slowly breathe in deeply. Can you feel any movement under your hands?

Now, put one hand down as far as you can between your shoulder-blades. Leave the other hand on your breastbone. Can you feel any movement in this upper part of your rib-cage?

To assess movement in the lower rib-cage, place one hand on the lowest part of the breastbone and the other over the bony border of the ribs at the back. Breathe slightly more deeply. What movement do you notice?

Finally, place one hand on either side of the lower rib-cage and assess the movement here.

You should now have an idea of **where** your breathing takes place. Are you breathing predominantly in the upper or lower part or does the whole of your rib-cage move when you breathe?

To confirm what you have felt, look at yourself in the mirror. Strip down to the waist so that you have a good view of your chest and abdomen. Loosen any tight clothing around your waist. Face the mirror and breathe. Where does the movement take place? Are you aware of any particular muscles? Now repeat this for both sides. You may need to take several breaths - some deeper than others.

Try this work with a partner. Instead of using your hands and a mirror, use their hands and eyes.

Once you have done this, you will want to assess how and where you are breathing at different times of the day:

- in the morning when you wake;
- driving to work;
- eating lunch;
- in a meeting;
- working at your desk, etc.

This will all help to develop your body awareness and illustrate how certain situations affect your breathing.

What affects breathing patterns?

Changes may occur in the rate and depth and/or the parts of the body you use to breathe. Due to the hormonal effects of the alarm response, breathing becomes more rapid when you are stressed, but posture, emotions and illness are also important influences on breathing patterns. When we have 'good' posture the body is balanced and poised, allowing movements to occur freely. For quiet, rhythmical breathing to occur throughout the rib-cage, the weight of the body must be taken through the spine and pelvis when sitting, and spine and legs if standing; this requires minimal muscle effort to maintain position and allows the rib-cage to move freely.

A lack of body awareness, of exercise and education and a sedentary lifestyle may mean that this balance is often missing. For example, it is common to see people hunched over their desks taking their body weight through the shoulders and elbows instead of the spine and pelvis. As they stabilise their shoulders, the muscles of the shoulder girdle become tensed as they take the body weight and participate in the movement of the upper rib-cage in breathing. This movement of the upper ribs is further exacerbated by the flexed, hunched sitting position restricting the diaphragm as the abdominal organs press upwards and the outward movement of the lower ribs is limited.

If fixed posture or tight shoulders become habitual then good lung and rib-cage expansion are restricted. People with such posture are working with mechanical disadvantages before they even encounter stressful situations, and they are less able to adapt.

Emotions, particularly those left unexpressed, have significant effects on breathing and breath control. When we react strongly to a situation and it makes us feel a certain way, we are usually able to express that reaction. However, it does not always seem appropriate to do this and so, subconsciously using breath control, we don't say anything, literally blocking the passage of air through our vocal cords. But sometimes these emotions or opinions may be expressed by using considerable control. You may then notice how the pitch and tone of the voice changes. Emotions may also be expressed in a gush of breath with anger and rage. You may have experienced a sudden shock or terror which results in a sudden intake of breath. This gasp may become 'locked-in' and, from then on, short, shallow breathing occurs in the upper chest.

When we are stressed it is not unusual for us to suppress our emotions more and more; often we're really not sure how we feel - we fear that if we did express ourselves we might let go and explode with anger or dissolve into tears. It often seems best just not to say anything. The problem is that the build-up is occurring internally and the awareness of how we really feel is lost as all feelings and reactions become suppressed - an example of the stress-spiral.

When this happens the diaphragm and abdominal muscles tighten, pulling the breastbone and ribs downwards. To expand the rib-cage and allow intake of breath, the neck and shoulder muscles have to work extra hard to overcome this downward force. Breathing may become rapid and shallow, as in hyperventilation, and the muscles become tight. The shoulders may also be pulled forward as a result.

Disease processes occurring in the lung can also affect the natural movement of the rib-cage. When lung tissue is damaged, the ribs and muscles obviously have to work harder to ventilate the lung. Smoking has many other well-known harmful effects, but it also disrupts breathing patterns. The smoker drags or sucks in air, using the upper ribs and muscles of the face and throat, not the diaphragm. Unfortunately this often persists as a breathing pattern. People who are suffering from pain also tend to breathe in short, shallow breaths as they attempt to save themselves from the pain.

A breath of change

Before developing relaxed breathing habits using the diaphragm, it is helpful to loosen up a bit with a few simple stretches for the shoulders, abdomen, neck and sides.

1) **The shoulders**

   Stand side on to the wall, place your outstretched hand against wall at shoulder height or just above. Move body slightly forward in front of the hand. Turn upper body slightly away from the hand, which will place stretch on the front of the shoulder joint.

   Breathe in, hold the position.
   Breathe out and turn away from the hand.
   Breathe in again, hold new position.
   Breathe out and turn a little further.
   Repeat for ten breaths on each side.
   If excessive discomfort is felt, discontinue exercise.

2) **Abdominal Stretch**

   Lie on your front.
   Slip elbows underneath you so you are lifted up by them.
   Feel contact of finger-tips and palms with the floor.
   Don't clench buttocks or hamstrings, simply let the back be supported between your elbows.
   Feel the stretch across your stomach.
   Breathe deeply five or six times.

NB To increase the stretch, place your hands where your elbows were and push up to support the back with straight arms.

If this exercise causes discomfort, discontinue.

3) **Neck stretch**

Sit and allow the head to drop forwards as far as it is comfortable.

Take the RIGHT ear towards the RIGHT shoulder.

Feel the stretch along the LEFT side of your neck.

Gently breathe in and out several times.

If **no** stretch is perceived it is possible to make this stronger by placing RIGHT hand and arm over the top and on to the back of the head and let its weight increase the stretch on the opposite side.

Repeat with the other side

4) **Side stretch**

Stand with feet shoulder-width apart.

Tuck your bottom in, and slightly bend knees.

Stretch your RIGHT arm up towards the ceiling.

Put your LEFT hand on your hip.

Lean towards the left, opening up your RIGHT side.

Keep the weight distributed equally between both feet.

Hold this position as you breathe in.

Breathe out and let the stretch yield further.

Breathe in again and hold position.

Breath out and let the stretch yield again.

Return to upright position.

Repeat to the other side and four or five times to both sides.

5) **Diaphragm breathing**

Initially, practise this lying down on a firm surface with a pillow to support the head in a comfortable position if necessary. Ultimately, this exercise can be done sitting, standing or lying.

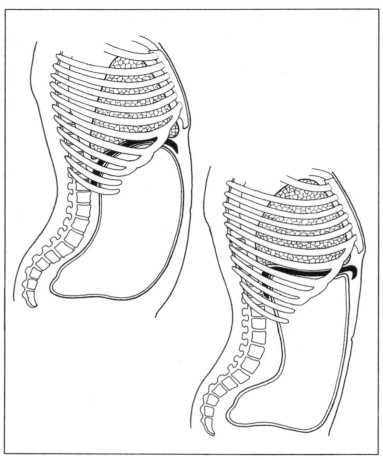

Start by imagining the position of the dome-shaped diaphragm. It may help to feel the bony borders of the ribs again where the diaphragm is attached.

Let your shoulders hang loose. As you start to breathe in, visualise that you are flattening the diaphragm by pushing the lower ribs out and contracting the muscle fibres that run outwards from the central tendon. You should feel a gentle increase in pressure in your abdomen, against your low back and into your pelvic floor. Imagine as you try this again that you are pushing the air down into the deeper part of your lungs. Your nostrils and face are completely relaxed as are your throat and shoulders. Become aware of the passage of air - does it flow down each nostril equally? If it doesn't, just be conscious of this and you will be surprised how this will correct itself.

As you breathe in again and think of flattening the diaphragm by allowing the bottom ribs to move outwards, imagine this outward movement taking place at the sides of all the ribs, starting at the bottom and, as your breaths get larger, moving all the way up to your sides, right up to under the armpits and neck; think of the front chest, the breastbone also moving away from your back as the air fills the space in between.
If this seems difficult, place both hands on your stomach, finger-tips touching. As the diaphragm flattens, drawing air into the lungs, you will notice that your stomach expands slightly as the finger-tips separate. Feel your sides and towards the back expanding also. Leave the mouth open, push the stomach out and feel the air being drawn in.

Breathing out should be a pleasure; just let it happen as the pelvic floor and abdominal wall gently contract to push the diaphragm back into its dome shape again. Enjoy the sighing feeling and relaxation it brings with it.

You can help this by pulling the stomach in from the sides by the action of the oblique and transverse abdominal muscles, but not using the flexing muscles of the abdomen. This helps support the low back.

Take time to practise this. Allow at least five minutes of uninterrupted time. This will improve body awareness and quieten the mind, establishing union between the two, as well as rewarding you with the benefits of relaxed breathing.

Checklist

☐ Why do I need to know about posture?

☐ Will I have more energy if I have 'good' posture?

☐ Do I know how I use my body?

☐ Which areas of my body become tight?

☐ Do I observe other people and their body use?

☐ Can I interpret people's mood and behaviour from their posture?

☐ How can I have balanced posture – standing?
　　　　　　　　　　　　　　　　　　　 – sitting?
　　　　　　　　　　　　　　　　　　　 – driving?
　　　　　　　　　　　　　　　　　　　 – lying down?

☐ Are my desk and chair suited to me?

Posture

'Posture' and 'deportment' are words seldom given consideration these days. It is unusual to see a poised and balanced posture or movements that appear easy and graceful in Western society. Educationally emphasis is placed on developing 'mind-use', not 'body-use' or awareness and even physical education seems to become less and less important.

Yet 'good' posture or body-use is balanced, requires minimal muscular effort to maintain and therefore, conserves energy. It's environmentally friendly if you like. When the body is relaxed and comfortable it allows greater freedom for the breathing muscles to expand the rib-cage.

Awareness of your posture and body-use is essential in managing pressure situations. The economical use of muscular effort associated with balanced posture results in fewer feelings of fatigue at the end of the day. Instead, because you look alert and ready for action, that is how you will behave. This is a positive self-image expressed through your posture and behaviour. You are balanced and grounded, so are less likely to encounter difficulties you are unable to cope with or be 'knocked off-balance'.

A businessman who attended one of our stress management courses tended to slump in his posture. A colleague at work always seemed to boss him around, asking him to perform the most trivial tasks. As he became more body aware and his posture improved, he noticed that his colleague ordered him about less. His body no longer looked vulnerable, his confidence had grown with this positive self-image and he no longer felt or acted in a subservient manner. Since then, when he comes under pressure, he makes a point of being aware of his posture to maintain his control of the situation and work to his best ability.

If we become stressed, several factors influence our posture. Due to hormonal effects preparing the body for 'action', muscles are tensed. Concentration on the task in hand, or mental anxiety and confusion, inhibit body awareness. Consequently, we may work in an awkward position, relying on muscle tension to hold this position for long periods of time. It is only when this becomes painful or we move that we notice how awkwardly we've been holding our body.

Emotions also influence our posture. Have you noticed how some people push their jaw forwards when they argue a point, or sit back and fold their arms when they feel defensive? Others store tension as they cross their legs, keeping their opinions to themselves, nails drumming on the desk with impatience or hands clenched in frustration. This added tension in the body further compounds the effects of stress. A tense body will react in that way, even though a situation may not warrant a reaction at all.

As muscles tense and/or fatigue, so poor posture becomes more pronounced. This is another stress-spiral - more energy is required to maintain a position so it depletes body reserves further. Breathing also becomes more difficult, either because the chest is compressed or is held too rigid, so greater muscular effort is required which causes further muscle fatigue.

You can become aware of your own posture by identifying areas in which muscles are vulnerable to tension; by observing yourself and others, by noticing how you use your body while sitting, standing, driving, etc. and by practising postural awareness exercises. This can often be a time of surprising discovery, as it was a lack of awareness that led to areas getting out of balance in the first place.

Relaxation

Before learning to relax you must first be able to recognise tension. Many people develop muscle tension and shortening over a number of years and are surprisingly unaware of where this has developed. In our osteopathic practice, it is a constant source of amazement among patients when we quickly identify areas of muscle tension and move parts of their body which have become very stiff, of which they were completely unaware. This section will help you identify some of these areas for yourself.

By feeling tense muscles, contracting and relaxing muscles by stretching and by observation, a picture emerges of how you use your body and where you store muscle tension. When doing the exercises below, compare the two sides of your body to determine the degree of balance between them. There are some sports and activities which may cause one side to become particularly dominant, e.g. racquet sports, or working at a corner-unit desk which results in movement always to one side. There are also less obvious ways, particularly as we express ourselves by our postures, in which uneven muscle tension develops.

■ *Discovery by touch*

Let's start by feeling tense muscles. As you sit at your desk rest your forearm on its edge. With your free hand feel the bicep which sits between the elbow and the shoulder. Push it about. Does it feel hard or soft? Now, put your hand under the desk top and push up as if you were going to lift it. Feel the bicep again. Is it hard or soft? Try this in different areas of your body. Work out which movements certain muscles control, e.g. the biceps muscle on the back of the arm between elbow and shoulder, the quadriceps muscle on the front of the leg between knee and hip. Explore your body as much as possible in this way to understand its design.

So now you have felt the contrast between relaxed and tensed muscle. When you become tense, muscles do not relax as they should; they feel hard all the time.

The neck and shoulders are common areas for muscle tension to develop. Feel the muscles across from your shoulder in towards the spine. Move up the back of the neck to the point where it reaches the base of the skull. Now include movement; as you feel, lift the shoulder to the ear, then as you feel the neck, let the head gently drop forwards. Repeat on the other side. How does it compare?

When writing this book we spent a great deal more time sitting down than usual, and sure enough muscle tension developed in our neck and shoulders. How does your muscle tension relate to your work position or activities? Explore other areas such as the back, buttocks and legs.

■ *Discovering by muscle contraction and relaxation*
We can also learn about body-use and improve awareness by contracting and relaxing muscles without feeling at the same time. This type of exercise is commonly used as a relaxation technique. It is important to discover relaxation techniques which suit you personally. At the end of this section are more relaxation techniques, as well as those described on the tape accompanying this book. If you don't find this particular exercise relaxing, don't worry, use it simply to learn more about your body.

Contracting and relaxing

■ *Preparation:*
Lie on your back, taking a little while to find a comfortable position. Loosen any tight clothing, take off your shoes, let your legs roll outwards and arms rest by sides with palms facing upwards.

As you breathe in tense your muscles, and as you breathe out let the muscles relax and focus on the word 'relax'.

■ *Feet and lower leg:*

Curl your toes towards the soles of your feet and point the feet downwards as you hold the feeling of tightness breathe in deeply. Hold it, hold it. Focus on the word 'relax' as you let the breath out and the muscles relax. Feel the lightness in the back of the calves. Now point your toes upwards and pull your feet up towards your shins. Breathe in deeply. Hold it, hold it. Focus on the word 'relax' and breathe out and enjoy the release of tension in the front of the shins.

■ *Hips and thighs:*

Start by pushing your heels into the floor. Breathe in deeply. Hold it, hold it. Focus on the word 'relax' and let the breath out. Feel the backs of the legs soften and float upwards. Now pull the kneecaps up and tense the front of the thighs. Breathe in deeply. Hold it, hold it. Focus on the word 'relax', let the breath out and relax the muscles.

■ *Stomach and diaphragm:*

Pull the stomach in as tight as you can. Take a deep breath in. Hold it, hold it. Focus on the word 'relax', let the breath out and let the stomach relax. This time, push the stomach out as far as you can, take a deep breath in. Hold it, hold it. Focus on the word 'relax', let the breath out and the diaphragm relax. Enjoy the sensation of letting go and relaxing.

■ *Back:*

Push your shoulders and neck down into the floor and arch the low back. Breathe in deeply. Hold it, hold it. Focus on the word 'relax' and enjoy the softness of your back as you breathe out.

■ *Arms:*

Clench your fist and push your arm down into the floor. Feel the tension. Breathe in deeply. Hold it, hold it. Focus on the word 'relax', breathe out and relax the muscles.

■ *Face and head*:
Screw up your face, wrinkle your forehead, squeeze your eyes tightly
together, purse your lips and clench your jaw. Take a deep breath in.
Hold it, hold it. Focus on the word 'relax' and as you are breathing out,
let your face relax, feel a warmth coming back over your head and face.

■ *Whole body*:
Finish by tensing the whole body up. Breathe in deeply. Hold it, hold
it. Focus on the word 'relax' as you breathe out and let your body
become limp and loose.

Discovery through observation

Begin to look at the way people move, like the dancer or athlete, the
chef on TV or the man repairing the road. Which muscles are they
using? Are they tensed or relaxed, graceful or awkward? Do their
movements appear effortless or forced? As you observe people in
this way, you will find you are able to tune into your own posture
and movement.

To look at yourself use a full-length mirror. Be interested in what
you see, not judgemental. If you become critical in a negative way,
try to let those ideas go. Don't dwell on them. Rather than
performing this observation in the office, we suggest the privacy of
your own home!

In a warm room, stand naked in front of a full-length mirror. Close
your eyes and imagine you are standing somewhere pleasant. Open
your eyes and keep the posture you have adopted as you run
through this checklist.

How is my head positioned?
Are my ear lobes level?
Is my head tilted to one side?
Is my head turned to one side?

Are the muscles of my neck tense?
Do they stand out on both sides, or only one side?

Are my shoulders drooped downwards or are they up towards my ears?
Are they pulled forwards or do I push them back?

Is my waist pulled in?
Does my stomach move as I breathe?

Rest your hands on the top of the pelvis at the side (hands on hips).
Are they level?
Does one side seem to fold more than the other?
Do my legs meet on the insides or bow outwards?
Are both kneecaps pointing in the same direction?
Are the muscles on my legs equal in size?

Are my feet pointing in the same direction or am I turning one out more than the other?
Do my big toes point straight ahead?
Do my toes make contact with the floor?

This list is to help you assess what you see. There may be other comparisons you will use to appreciate your posture. When you're out and about, observe your movements in shop-windows and glass doors. See if you move with ease.

It is important not to get carried away by what you see. There is no right or wrong way to be. Observation is only a small part of becoming aware of your posture.

The curves of the spine

The spine is the central mast of the body, supporting the head, rib-cage and shoulders, distributing the weight down through the pelvis, legs and feet. It has adopted a shape of three curves: two forwards in the neck and low back and one backwards in the upper back (dorsal area). This is a dynamic shape with shock absorbing properties. Therefore, if you are too stiff and upright, you won't have the same accommodating 'give' in your body.

The curve backwards (or **kyphosis**) creates extra space in the thorax for the heart and lungs. However, if this becomes exaggerated, the compensation made by the curve forwards (or **lordosis**) of the neck and low back experience strain.

Becoming aware of your posture is a step towards balancing the spine and reducing muscle tension through the body.

■ *The upright posture (decreased curves)*
This posture is often mistaken for 'good posture'. People who look upright pride themselves on their carriage but it is often stiff and rigid with an undynamic spine that does not allow for free and easy movement.

It is characterised by straightening of the forward curve of the neck and low back and the backward curve of the upper back. The chin is firmly tucked in, the shoulder blades are pulled back and the pelvis drops too far back. This makes it difficult for the lower ribs and diaphragm to work and breathing takes place more in the upper chest, placing extra mechanical strain on the neck muscles. The abdominal muscles are tensed, impairing the action of the diaphragm. Muscle tension is used to sustain unnatural erectness. This increased tension causes unnecessary wear and tear on the body. Surprisingly, this is the classic 'guardsman' stance.

■ *The slumped posture (increased curves)*
This posture has a feeling of defeat about it, as if gravity has overcome the strength of the muscles. Everything seems to sag. It is particularly associated with people who sit or drive for long periods of time. As the body is flexed in these positions, the backward curve of the upper back is increased by muscle tightness or shortening of the front shoulder muscles, rib-cage and stomach. As a result, the weight of the shoulders fall in a downwards and forward direction, so in order to maintain an upright position, the muscles at the back of the neck tighten to bring the head upright and similarly the muscles of the low back tighten to bring the torso

into an upright position. This increase in the forward curve leads to early wear and tear, muscle fatigue, restricted movement of the diaphragm and an increase in pressure on to the abdomen. In addition this posture requires more energy and effort to maintain than balanced posture.

Balanced posture

■ *Standing*

There is an easy balanced posture which is both noticeable to others and to ourselves. Essentially you feel relaxed in your movements, there is a lightness in your limbs and a spring in your step. There is an unforced lengthening in your whole body and a feeling that breathing is unencumbered as your ribs rise and fall. The shoulders are relaxed and you can feel the weight of the arms falling from them. The head is carried lightly on the neck and shoulders, and the highest point is the crown of the head rather than the forehead. The weight of the torso is taken through the legs equally to the feet, knees are straight but not forced back. The toes are not tensed but lightly in contact with the ground.

It all sounds marvellous doesn't it? But how do we achieve this?

Well, let's go back to the fundamentals. We've already stated that good posture requires balance. The body balances its weight over the stable base provided by points of contact with the surface below. When we stand, the soles of the feet are the contact areas. For good balance it is important that the weight is distributed evenly between both feet and between the front and the back of the sole of each foot.

Stand up. Imagine you are standing in wet sand. How would your footprints look? Would the footprints be equal, reflecting even weight distribution?

The soles of the feet are richly supplied with sensory nerve-endings informing the body about the conditions of the surface below. If we walk on uneven ground, the sensory nerve-endings monitor this and the appropriate muscles can be used to compensate.

Similarly, if we stand on one foot, to stop us falling over various muscles throughout the body tighten and shorten to compensate for the imbalance created. The compensation is as a result of the information from the sole of the supporting foot. This muscle compensation can occur when not physically necessary, leaving he body unbalanced.

To recreate balance, a certain amount of relearning is necessary. Conscious effort should be made to distribute the body weight evenly between both feet. To achieve this, more attention should be directed to the foot which is usually under the least pressure. Imagine you are pushing this foot into the ground each time you become conscious of your feet.

Having balanced the body between both feet, balance the weight between the ball of the foot and the heel. Gently rock back and forth. Relax the knees, don't lock them back. Tuck your bottom in and think of lengthening the back all the way up the spine to the crown of your head. Don't force yourself up. Relax the shoulders.

The most well-known pioneer of postural education was Frederick M. Alexander, who developed the Alexander Technique. He believed that the alignment of the head with the spine was the crucial factor in establishing good posture. From his work the useful points to remember are:

(1)   keep the neck loose and free;
(2)   with the ears as a pivot, drop the head forward;
(3)   ease the head upwards as if it were suspended from the ceiling by a fine thread;
(4)   allow the back simultaneously to lengthen and widen.

When you initiate any movement, start by easing the head upwards keeping the head balanced and allowing the body to follow the direction of the movement. Combine this with an awareness of your weight distribution through your contact point with the surface below.

The following exercise will help you become aware of the features of your own standing posture.

The wall exercise

Stand with your feet at hip distance apart with the heels close to a wall. As you gently sway back against the wall the shoulders and buttocks should make contact simultaneously. If one shoulder or one buttock makes contact before the other there may be a twist in your posture.

If your shoulders touch first before your buttocks, you may have an exaggerated curve in your upper spine. Alternatively if your buttocks are first in contact, this suggests that the pelvis is being carried too far back.

The hair on the back of your head should just brush against the wall. If the back of your head is pressed against the wall, nod your head slightly. Once you are happy with your posture, walk away from the wall maintaining this feeling of poised, erect posture.

NB **Flattening the forward curve of the low back against the wall is a useful exercise for strengthening the abdominal muscles and encouraging them to support the low back.**

■ *At work*

As part of your job you may have to stand up and present information to colleagues or clients. Taking a moment to consider your posture will not only enhance your presentation in terms of confidence and the tone and quality of your voice, but will also help with any slight nervousness. Basically, do this by 'grounding' yourself, i.e. thinking about the contact your feet are making and then easing your posture upwards and outwards from there.

If your work involves long periods of standing, balanced posture is essential to avoid fatigue and unnecessary wear and tear. If you use repetitive movements, try to use both sides of your body equally.

■ Sitting

When sitting, the weight of the body is no longer taken by the soles of the feet but on the sit bones of the pelvis. These are bony prominances which provide a broad base and points of contact on which to balance.

To find them, lift your bottom and sit back down on your fingers. Sit up slightly and rock back and forth. You will feel the harder bony surface of your sit bones against your fingers.

To sit with balanced posture, the weight of your body should be equally balanced between the left and right and both feet should be firmly supported. As with standing, it is not unusual to favour one side more than the other. To find out if you do this, shut your eyes and put all your weight on to your right sit bone. Does this feel comfortable and secure? Now, take your weight through the left sit bone. How does this compare? Is it easier or more difficult? Often it is difficult to feel one side as much as the other. Your body is used to arranging your weight over your favoured sit bone. Although the pattern is familiar, the body is not balanced. Consciously redistribute your weight between both sit bones.

Once you have done this, the next stage is to balance the spine between both sit bones. By rolling your pelvis forward you will feel your sit bones pushing down into the surface below. Don't arch your back or pull your shoulders back to achieve this. As you roll your pelvis forward, feel your spine easing upwards. Allow the back of your neck to lengthen and balance the head as for standing.

■ Desks and chairs

When working in a sitting position the design of your desk and chair is a major contributing factor to your sitting posture. The height of the desk should allow your legs to sit comfortably underneath and should not be much higher than your elbows. A tilted desk top prevents excessive flexion of the head and reduces strain on the neck.

When typing, in order to prevent aches in the shoulder, neck and head, the forearms need to be supported while maintaining a relaxed shoulder position. You don't have to lift your shoulders to bend your elbows! The position of items to be typed or the screen of the VDU should be varied so that the head is not always inclined in the same direction.

The chair should be as close to the desk as possible, while enabling you to maintain a relaxed arm position. The chair seat should allow the feet to be in contact with the floor. The thighs should remain parallel with the floor. The support the chair seat offers must be flat and firm so that it is easy to find the points of contact. The seat width must support the soft thigh without digging in. The chair back must provide support for the lower back.

Recently, the design of some chairs has been radically altered by sloping the sitting surface forwards and downwards. This encourages the weight of sitting to be taken down through the sit bone and helps prevent the slumped posture which strains the low back. Using a foam wedge to change the angle of the sitting surface has similar benefits. But remember, a good chair is only a start to balanced sitting posture.

If the slope of the sitting surface is down and back, the pelvis rolls back and the weight is taken by the low back curving backwards. This is contrary to the natural design of the low back and often results in low backache. This situation occurs when sitting in soft easy chairs; so always encourage the natural forward curve of your low back by supporting it with a cushion.

■ Driving

How often do we think about comfort and car-seat design when buying a car? Most of us are more interested in the style, engine size and all the little extras! However, test driving a prospective new car for at least half an hour is essential to ensure that it is really going to be comfortable for you.

Check that the seat is firm, providing support for the low back, with sides that maintain comfort while cornering. The back of the thighs should be supported by the seat but this should not cause pressure on the back of the knees. The seat should be fully adjustable to ensure easy reach of the steering-wheel.

Before driving off always check that your seat is adjusted to a comfortable position, that your mirrors provide good visibility and that you do not have to strain your neck to use them. Make sure your bottom is well back in the seat, thus providing maximum comfort for the low back. Most seats slope downwards and backwards which makes it difficult to sit on the sit bones of your pelvis and keep the natural curves of the spine. If a lower back curve is not naturally present in the seat, use a lumbar roll to counteract this.

Hold the steering-wheel firmly but not tightly. Let the elbows hang down and drop the shoulders. The neck should ease upwards as the head nods slightly forward.

If you know how long your journey will take and you are late in leaving for an appointment, nothing can alter the fact that you are going to be late. So once in the car, calm down, practise your abdominal breathing and make the most of the opportunity to collect your thoughts to ensure that you don't feel flustered on your arrival.

■ *Lying*
When you lie on your back on a firm surface you might naturally suppose that the back of the head, shoulders, rib-cage, back buttocks, thighs, calves and heels would all have a uniform contact with the surface. However, as we know, tension is carried in our muscles without our conscious knowledge, and it distorts this uniformity. By becoming aware of how we are lying, we can identify areas where an imbalance has developed. As muscles relax so uniform contact becomes more apparent.

Try this exercise.

Lie on a comfortable but firm surface. Loosen tight clothing and take off your shoes. Use a thin pillow if you need to. Ask yourself if you feel you are lying on a flat surface. There will normally be a small gap between your low back and the floor. Do you have equal contact on the left and right sides? Compare the heels, calves, thighs, buttocks, back, shoulders, elbows, forearms, hands and finally the back of your head. If it feels as though one side has less contact, push down slightly into the surface. Then recheck.

This is an extremely useful way of preparing for sleep when lying in bed.

Relaxation and awareness techniques

Checklist

Select the exercises which work best for you and incorporate them in your daily routine.

Wake up

Eye 1

Eye 2

Toe and foot stretch

Toes and breathing

Driving

Neck

Shoulders

Hands

Breathing and low back

At the office

Five-minute stretch

Floppy doll

Quick relaxation

Eye exercises

Deep relaxation

Meditation

Using the accompanying tape

Get a piece of the action!

Here are a selection of exercises and routines to help develop your body awareness and relaxation skills. Select the ones you enjoy most and take time to learn them. By including them in your daily routine you will be able to make the most of pressure and avoid the undesirable effects of stress.

■ *Create a fashion!*

Gain the support of your family and work colleagues. Tell them what you are doing and why. Your enthusiasm will encourage them to follow suit. Be supportive of any of your workmates or employees who also want to use the techniques. If everyone's doing it, it soon becomes the fashion!

Wake up exercises

We all vary in 'how' we wake up: some are early birds and are awake instantly; others take longer and have various rituals to perform before they consider themselves 'up'! But either way it is likely that if you become stressed your sleep pattern will be disrupted. You may find it difficult to get going in the morning. These next few exercises allow you to reconnect with your mind and body after a night's sleep. They prepare your body for the day and help 'ground' you. We all too often leap from our beds and run through the day from that moment on. Let's start with some eye exercises.

Eye exercising

These exercises come from the ancient Taoist religion and are part of a complex system of spiritual doctrines and philosophies. Here, you will find the exercises very helpful in awakening tired eyes in the morning or during the day, particularly if you have been doing a lot of close work or working with a VDU screen.

■ *Exercise 1*

Look at the illustration below and begin by placing the thumbs on point A. Press quite hard. It is likely to be very tender. When you have been practising this exercise for a while these points should no longer feel painful and the eyes will be in good health once again. Press deeply for about ten seconds, then rub the point. Work through points B-E, pressing first and then

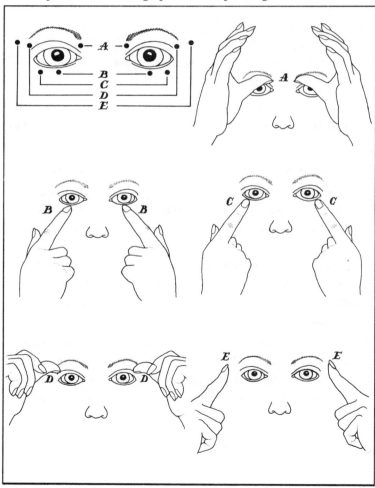

massaging. Repeat for three rounds (A-E). Then starting from the nose side of the eye, circle around the brow to the temple, returning along the cheekbone. Massage for several seconds.

Finally, rub the heel of the hands together hard to create warmth between the two. Place the hand over the eyes and forehead enjoying the sensation of warmth.

■ *Exercise 2*

This will improve your peripheral vision and awareness.
Look straight ahead with the head level. Begin by looking slowly up to the ceiling and then slowly down to the floor. Repeat several times.

Next, look from side to side. Be sure to let the eyes move as far as possible. Now move the eyes in the two diagonal planes into opposite corners.

Finally, rotate the eyes clockwise and then anti-clockwise.

Each exercise should be repeated several times. This will take about ten minutes when practised slowly. End by rubbing the palms together and bathing the eyes with warmth as in Exercise 1.

Before you step out of bed get in touch with your big toe, toes and feet. Bring the big toe up towards your shin. Pull it up hard. Breathe in and as you breathe out, curl the toe back towards the sole of your foot. Repeat several times.

Have you noticed how animals really stretch after they have been asleep? Well, we need to do that too. So have a really good stretch in bed before stepping out. Push the left leg down, feel the stretch in the back of your leg. Repeat with the right. Stretch the arms out one at a time, wriggle your body around and become aware of your back and shoulders.

You're now ready to step out of bed. Let your feet make contact with the floor and stand up.

Take a couple of deep breaths. As you breathe in, curl the toes up towards you, and as you breathe out, push the toes down into the floor. This will literally help you keep your feet on the ground through the day. Focus on the contact your feet are making with the ground. Is the weight evenly distributed between both feet? If you find yourself in a tense or nerve-racking situation during the day, remember to use this technique.

Finally, while you are having your morning shower or bath, use the time wisely to massage your body, particularly the scalp and base of the skull. Enjoy the sensation of water on your skin and back.

These exercises are very simple and easy to build into your morning routine. Clients of ours who have used them have been surprised at the pleasure they now experience when waking up and beginning a new day.

Driving

Having considered your posture and body position while driving, you can now practise a couple of exercises and ideas, particularly if you drive in built-up areas where there is slow-moving traffic, frequent junctions or traffic lights.

While driving your movements tend to be restricted by the position of the foot and hand controls, and by your head position looking straight ahead. This results in hardly any change in your body position. Therefore, if any opportunity presents itself when the car is stationary, perform these few exercises:

(1) *For your neck.*

Perform the stretches as described before breathing, by turning your head from side to side and nodding the head up and down.

Perform this slowly, synchronising your breathing and allowing time for the muscles to stretch at the limit of each movement.

(2) Shoulders

Raise the shoulders gently to your ears. Hold. Let them go and think 'relax'. Feel the weight of the arms pulling down.

(3) Hands

Spread the fingers, stretch them out. Relax. Now clench them into a fist. Relax. Repeat this three times.

(4) Breathing

Practise diaphragmatic breathing. Tense the abdominal muscles as you breathe out. This gives support to the low back. Always check your points of contact with the car seat; is your body weight evenly distributed to both sit bones?

Relax muscles that aren't needed for driving, such as those around the jaw, shoulders and hands. Slow down, take your foot off the pedal. Fast driving requires more concentration and can leave you feeling tired.

During the journey select tapes or CDs which you know are relaxing.

On long journeys, stop every hour-and-a-half to stretch. Get out and walk around the car. When you arrive at your destination you will feel considerably more alert.

Techniques for the office

We have focused particularly on the office as a place to practise exercises for awareness and relaxation because this is often where the tension build-up begins. Adjusting to new routines takes a while so for the first three or four weeks timetable in your exercises. Write it in your diary. Tell your staff or secretary, colleagues or boss. Divert interruptions for that time. Make a chart with your exercises on it and tick them off.

If you want to check your breathing and posture every hour, use any gadget such as the bleep on your watch or an alarm clock to remind you to do so. Use absolutely anything that will help you in the first few weeks.

Once these exercises become habit and you are enjoying the benefits, less effort will be needed.

The key to keeping pressure under control is to ensure these exercises are included in your routine even when you are feeling good:

(a) five-minute stretch routine;
(b) floppy doll;
(c) quick relaxation;
(d) Eye exercises.

■ *a)* *Five-minute stretch routine*

Loosen your clothing, take off your jacket and remove high-heeled shoes. Sit back in your chair with your low back well supported. Place both feet on the floor.

Breathe in slowly and as you breathe out become aware of your body position. Repeat several times.

Let the head drop forward, stretching the muscles along the back of your neck. Slowly move the head back to look at the ceiling. Repeat three times. On the third time, feel this stretch into the upper back and spine.

Turn the head from side to side slowly. Using the breathing, feel the end of the stretch with the 'out' breath. Repeat three times.

Roll the right shoulder back, down, round and up in a circular movement. Follow with the left shoulder and alternate between the two shoulders. Feel the stretch as they slowly move. Repeat three times.

Let both arms drop to the sides. Lean over to the right. Let the head follow. Don't go so far that you feel you're about to fall. Feel the stretch down the left side. Repeat to the other side. Repeat three times.

Now stand side-on to your desk or chair. Place one hand on the desk or back of the chair to steady yourself. Lift the heel of the opposite foot towards your bottom. Hold this ankle with the free hand. Feel the stretch in the front of the thigh. This muscle becomes shortened when you are sitting for long periods of time.

Do not arch the low back. To prevent this, slightly bend the knee of the supporting leg. Breathe in and, as you breathe out, feel the muscle lengthening. Repeat with the other leg. Repeat three times.

It is important to perform repetitions **three** times as, on the third stretch, you will often notice the most lengthening. Use the breath out to lengthen the muscle groups. Never force a muscle to stretch if you are experiencing considerable discomfort or pain.

■ *b)* **Floppy doll**

This is an excellent exercise when you feel tired and your shoulders are aching.

Move your chair away from your desk. Loosen your waistband or belt. Come slightly forward in your chair with feet firmly on the ground. Arms hanging to your sides. Very, very slowly let the head come forwards, follow with the shoulders into the curve. Feel one vertebra at a time curling forwards. When you come to a tight area, stop. Breathe into it and let it go as you breathe out. Curl down as far as comfortable. Hold this position and breathe slowly and deeply three or four times. Now slowly, very slowly begin your uncurl. Returning, one vertebra at a time, to your upright position.

■ *c)* *Quick relaxation*

Sit back in your chair with low back well supported and your feet firmly on the ground. Breathe slowly, deeply for several moments. Let peace and calm come to you.

Begin with your left leg. As you breathe in, imagine the air comes in through the toes and travels up in the leg to the chest; and as you breathe out, that it leaves the chest down the leg and out through the toes again. Repeat three times and then with the right leg.

Move to the arms. Imagine the breath comes in through the finger-tips, travels up through the arm to the chest and out along the same route. Repeat three times on each arm.

Once you have mastered this, combine the flow of breath through the arms and legs simultaneously. Feel the warmth and lightness this brings to your body. When you have completed this exercise you will feel relaxed and refreshed and ready to continue work.

■ **d)** *Eye exercises*

These were described in the previous section (on pages 70 and 71) and may be found to be useful to try at work.

■ Relaxation

As the body muscles relax, the mind relaxes and this helps reduce sympathetic nervous system activity which in turn reduces heart-rate and lowers blood pressure. Research has shown that people who practise regular relaxation exercises for a month or more will have significantly lowered their blood cholesterol and other fat. In other words, their alarm response has not been firing so often, releasing hormones, etc.

We have produced a tape to accompany this book which covers many of the exercises outlined here, as well as several others, all designed to enhance awareness and relaxation.

If you have not done relaxation exercises before, please allow yourself time to learn them and don't expect too much too soon. Though the benefits are not instant, the results are well worth waiting for. The next exercise is one which is included on the tape.

■ *Deep relaxation*

Preparation: Spend time getting comfortable. Loosen tight clothing. Kick off your shoes. Lie on your back on a firm surface with the feet slightly apart, arms next to the body with palms turned slightly upwards. Keep the eyes closed and let the breathing fall into a natural rhythm. Allow the floor to support you so your muscles can become relaxed. Let the knees and legs turn out. Is your neck and head comfortable?

Jaw: Open your mouth, let your jaw hang loose. Move it from side to side. Breathe in and slowly out through your mouth. Let your mouth lightly close.

Breathing: Take a deep breath now and, as you breathe out, say to yourself 'relax and let go'. You are comfortable, let your body become heavy. Breathe in again, briefly pause and let the breath gently slip from you as you say to yourself 'relax and let go'. Feel the breathing become deep. Use the abdominal muscles with the diaphragm, the breath supporting the length of your spine.

Body Aware: Become aware of your whole body as you continue breathing and becoming more relaxed. Keep your eyes closed, your jaw loose, teeth slightly apart. We are going to work through each area of the body. Start at your feet or the top of your head, whichever you prefer.

Feet and toes: Become aware of each of your toes individually. Then notice the soles of your feet, the contact your heels are making with the underlying surface. Breathe in and as you breathe out, think 'relax and let go'. Feel them become warm and comfortable.

Legs: Now move up the front of your legs and down the back. How do they feel? Breathe into them and say to yourself 'relax and let go'.

Hips and Buttocks: Let your legs fall into the most comfortable position. Relax your buttocks. Feel the small of your back against the floor. Breathe in and as you breathe out think 'relax and let go'.

Back and Stomach: Is your back comfortable against the floor? Relax the muscles. You are comfortable, safe and secure. Breathe into any tight areas. Breathe in and as you breathe out think 'relax and let go'.

Chest, Shoulders and Arms: Become aware of the movement of the chest as the breath moves in and out. Feel the shoulders against the floor and the arms to your side. Breathe in and as you breathe out think 'relax and let go'.

Head and face: Now breathe into the back of your neck and up towards the base of the skull. Feel the back of the head against the floor. Let the muscles of your face relax, the forehead feels wider and higher, the eyebrows are relaxed. The cheeks are soft and the lips are loose. Breathe in and as you breathe out think 'relax and let go'.

Deeper: Scan your whole body. You are completely relaxed. With each breath you become more deeply relaxed. Imagine each breath rippling through your body. Your body feels light and you feel free and floating. Energy is all around you. Peaceful and calm. Let the words echo in your mind. You are content and secure. Breathe in and out as you say to yourself 'my mind and body are one'.

Returning: Let the feeling wash over you that your mind and body are as one in peaceful, calm surroundings. You are going to use this feeling when you get up. Now count from one to three. On three you will be refreshed, wide awake and ready to go. One, you feel calm and relaxed but alert. Two, you are mentally awake. Three, your eyes are open, you are refreshed and ready to go. Wiggle your fingers and toes. Move your legs and arms. Roll on to your side. Breathe in and out. Now come up into a sitting position. Smile. When you are standing, breathe in, raise the toes towards your shins, and as you breathe out, push them down into the floor. Repeat three times.

You are now relaxed, balanced and grounded. You couldn't be in better shape!

Meditation

Meditation is simply a way of calming the mind. The mind is made up of two hemispheres - the left hemisphere is the more active in planning, organising, doing mathematical-type jobs, while the right side of the brain is a more creative or an intuitive centre.

In meditation we give the mind, particularly the left side, something to chew on, usually a repetitive sound such as 'one' or 'om'. This allows the mind to slow down and become less active. It is repeated over and over again. If thoughts come and stop this, just re-focus on the sound. Doing this regularly will allow the right side of your brain to be more in balance with your left. You will be able to be a witness to your own sensations; and, naturally, you will suffer less from 'hurry' sickness, a condition where you always feel pressurised or in a rush.

Medically, it will have the benefit of reducing blood pressure, decreasing the amount of arousal in your sympathetic nervous system and producing a deeply relaxing state which is ideal for replenishing the body's depleted stores.

Practical Meditation

It is best to sit in a comfortable chair in a warm place. Don't allow any interruptions for twenty minutes, try to make space for two sessions per day, morning and evening. Start by just repeating the sound in your mind, over and over again. Don't use an alarm clock to stop you after twenty minutes, just judge the time. It doesn't need to be exact. If thoughts about the shopping or what you need to do next crop up, just let them float out by thinking of the sound again and again.

Section 3:
PRESSURE OR STRESS?

Checklist

☐   Know the role of perception.

☐   Identify your trigger words/phrases.

☐   Know what factors at work cause pressure to become stress.

☐   Understand the influence of life events.

☐   Know how to identify stress in others.

Identifying stressors
Getting to the point!

We have recognised the symptoms of stress, quietened the mind to gain objectivity and thus allowed ourselves to break out of the 'stress-spiral'. We will now use a personal stress survey and look at some of the potential causes of stress. You may be familiar with the idea of stress questionnaires, which are a useful tool, but they do not extract a personalised understanding and perception of why you as an individual find certain situations stressful.

The list of potential stressors is limitless. There may be times when these are actually of use to us, creating simply a 'pressure' situation. However, too many factors at any one time will develop into a stress situation. It may be argued that any change or adaptation in life has the potential to produce a stress response. It is important to remember that not all the stressors identified will necessarily be stress-inducing to all individuals.

Depending on how a person interprets a situation due to their culture, environmental and genetic make-up, so it may or may not be a source of stress. For example Christmas is an event which some people find a relaxing, enjoyable experience, while others find it one of the most stressful times of the year. Why is this? It really does depend on your perception of the situation; you may have to put up with an interfering relative, suffer a lack of finances or worry how you will fit everyone into your house, all of which may begin the stress build-up. It is no coincidence that the period immediately after Christmas is a common time for people to commence divorce proceedings.

Research has revealed that certain common events in people's lives have the capacity to cause distress; these are major life events. However, more subtle and elusive is the exposure to repeated minor sources of stress, e.g. a crowded tube journey to work, poor environmental conditions, or a difficult relationship either at work or at home. On an accumulative scale these may be even more detrimental in leading to a decline in health and effective work performance.

Understanding ourselves and knowing our abilities are vital prerequisites to handling pressure effectively. From the personal stress survey determine your three trigger words/phrases. These will allow you to review major life events and the more subtle sources of stress discussed in the remainder of this chapter.

A personal stress survey

This is the most testing section of the book, but it can also be the most rewarding. Allow yourself at least half an hour to answer the questions. Ask those around you to give you this time without interruptions. Prepare your mind by sitting quietly and performing your favourite breathing/relaxation exercise. If at any time you are finding the survey difficult simply stop, repeat the exercise and try again. Use the worked example to help you.

(a) Think of an occasion when you were stressed at home.

(b) Think of an occasion at home which did not stress you.

(c) Think of the worst thing that could realistically happen at work.

Think about situation (a). Try and remember how it made you feel and write down your feelings on a piece of paper. Repeat the procedure for situation (b) and situation (c).

Identify what it is about each situation that created those feelings. Did you have any feelings that were common to more than one situation? If so, what factor that created those feelings was common to both situations? Write down a word or phrase identifying this factor. This is your **first** trigger word or phrase. Now, ask yourself what is your opposite to this word, not necessarily a dictionary opposite.

If you did not have any feelings that were common to more than one situation, select a situation that appears to be the odd one out.

You may not know why you select a particular one but just follow your intuition. Add this to your list of feelings associated with this situation.

What factors were behind these feelings?

Write down the opposites to these factors.

Select the most significant factor and its opposite. This is your **first** trigger word.

Work the whole scheme through substituting (a), (b), (c) with (d), (e), (f) to determine your **second** trigger word, and with (h), (i), (j) to determine your **third** word.

(d) Think of an important event in the last six months that was not stressful.

(e) Think of the most recent stress-inducing event that springs to mind.

(f) Think of an event in the last year that was stressful.

(g) Think of an activity or hobby you enjoy.

(h) Think of a routine event that you find stressful.

(i) Think of a routine activity you do not find stressful.

■ *The personal stress survey*

(a)	Situation:	....
	Feelings:	....
	Factors:	....
(b)	Situation:	....
	Feelings:	....
	Factors:	....
(c)	Situation:	....
	Feelings:	....
	Factors:	....

Common link/odd one out:
Trigger word/phrase 1:
        Opposite:

(d)	Situation:	....
	Feelings:	....
	Factors:	....
(e)	Situation:	....
	Feelings:	....
	Factors:	....
(f)	Situation:	....
	Feelings:	....
	Factors:	....

Common link/odd one out:
Trigger word/phrase 2:
        Opposite:

(g)	Situation:	....
	Feelings:	....
	Factors:	....
(h)	Situation:	....
	Feelings:	....
	Factors:	....
(i)	Situation:	....
	Feelings:	....
	Factors:	....

Common link/odd one out:
Trigger word/phrase 3:
        Opposite:

■ Worked example of the personal stress survey for Tom

(a) Situation: *Taking work home causing argument with partner*
    Feelings: *Confusion, not being understood, angry*
    Factors: *Divided loyalty, beyond own control*

(b) Situation: *Friends staying for the weekend*
    Feelings: *Happiness, relaxed, laughter*
    Factors: *Pleasure of providing*

(c) Situation: *Failed to arrive at important meeting*
    Feelings: *Embarrassment, failure, incompetence*
    Factors: *Mismanagement of time, disorganised*

Common link/odd one out: (a) and (c) **Lack of control**
                         Opposite: **Control**

(d) Situation: *Christening of second child*
    Feelings: *Enjoyment, happiness*
    Factors: *Pride*

(e) Situation: *Sitting in traffic jam - late for appointment*
    Feelings: *Frustrated, angry, hemmed in*
    Factors: *Events imposed*

(f) Situation: *Death of father*
    Feelings: *Sadness, grief, loss*
    Factors: *Loss of parental security*

Common link/odd one out: (e) **Frustrated**   Not frustrated
                             Angry   Calm
                             Hemmed in   Free

                   Opposite: **Not frustrated**

(g) Situation: *Walking in the countryside*
    Feelings: *Solitude, satisfying*
    Factors: *Change of environment*

(h) Situation: *Phone calls causing interruptions*
    Feelings: *Irritation, disturbing, annoying*
    Factors: *Taking up time*

(i) Situation: *Making the bed*
    Feelings: *Minor achievement*
    Factors: *Creating some order but does not take long*

Common link/odd one out: (h) and (i)   **Time**
                   Opposite: **Enough time**

Using your trigger words/phrases

Determining your trigger words/phrases is a simple way of gaining insight into what type of situations you may find threatening and what elements may cause a pressure situation to escalate into a stressful one. A situation to which all three trigger words/phrases may be applied will contain stress.

From Tom's worked example we can see that being out of control of a situation, frustration and lack of time to deal with the problem cause him stress.

Tom is a busy advertising executive who manages the accounts allocated to him with effectiveness and flair. Thus, when Rachel, a member of another team, is unable to make a presentation to potential new clients due to a throat infection, Tom is asked at the last minute to step in. He accepts but soon finds he has indigestion, a tight chest, clammy hands and the start of a nagging headache. He is unable to speak to Rachel on the phone to gain some brief on the presentation, has little time to prepare, and becomes frustrated - particularly as this executive has been known to slip off for the odd day in order to play golf. As a result of the short space of time available in which to prepare, Tom makes an uncharacteristically mediocre presentation. He staggers through the rest of the day, chasing his tail and arrives home feeling exhausted, wound up and very dissatisfied.

We are able to see how, among other elements - lack of control, frustration and lack of time, Tom's three trigger words/phrases were present. His usual pressurised environment in which he enjoys success became stressful and led to a very unsatisfactory, unrewarding day.

Tom is lucky though, after a good night's sleep he'll probably put this all behind him and carry on enjoying his work. However, if these type of events occurred over a prolonged period of time, the long-term effect of stress on his health would become apparent.

The **frequency** and the **duration** of the factors which are perceived as stressful are the key in determining the outcome of a person's behaviour and health. This may involve not one factor but many.

As you read through the remainder of this chapter, keep your trigger words/phrases in mind. Use them to help you identify which events and sources of stress at work, in your environment and socially, are relevant to you. Adapt this list or add to it to gain a complete personal picture.

Checklist

☐ What does the job involve?

☐ Are the work conditions favourable?

☐ How do you get along with the people you work with?

or/

☐ Do you feel you have good working relationships?

Pressure not stress at work

The delicate balance at work may be threatened by certain factors which have been found to increase stress. They may be identified by asking three questions.

(1)   What does the job involve?

(2)   Are the work conditions favourable?

(3)   Do you get along with the people you work with?

or/ Do you feel you have good working relationships?

Consider these questions to evaluate whether or not there are factors which may be potential sources of stress. Keep your trigger words/phrases in mind.

Take a moment in a general meeting to discuss these questions with your colleagues or boss. There may be a common factor that you all find unsatisfactory which will be dealt with more effectively as a group rather than individually.

When a job comes up for which you are recruiting a new employee, these questions will be useful in terms of pressure and stress in determining what **you** have to offer and **who** will fit in best with the existing set-up.

These questions all seem quite obvious when you are considering a job. However, here we are asking you to assess the answers in terms of your trigger words/phrases which in turn will help you determine the factors which potentially could cause stress.

What does the job involve?

AREA	FACTORS	For me is there: YES/NO	For my staff is there: YES/NO
Career development	Interest Stimulation Satisfaction Broadening of education Sufficient training Security Potential promotion		
Workload	Clear definition of tasks Reasonable workload Realistic targets/deadlines Control over work Frequent change New technology High expectations Perfectionism		
Responsi-bilities	To clients To colleagues (the team within the hierarchy) – above – below Defined limits of authority Discipline		
Communica-tions	Clear aims and objectives Involvement with decision - making Paperwork Travelling		

Whether your answers are 'Yes' or 'No', briefly consider their significance in relation to your trigger words or phrases. For instance, using Tom's trigger words to assess the career development of his job, we see that so long as he can exercise control, has enough time and doesn't experience frustrating delays or relationships, he will continue to enjoy his work. However, if for example he felt he really needed additional training of some kind, but either he perceived he couldn't afford the time or it was beyond his control to arrange the training, then a situation of stress may develop.

Let's use another common trigger phrase 'being seen as inefficient'. This perception sometimes creates stress in people with respect to their workload. If people are not **seen** to be productive, they often feel they may be seen as being inefficient, similarly, if they don't adapt to new technology or are unclear about deadlines. It is easy to see how the fear of being exposed begins to become stressful and problems result.

Trigger words relating to feelings and expressions of emotion will often be particularly applicable to communication and responsibility at work - that skilled but elusive art of dealing with the human race. How do your chosen trigger words relate to these sections?

Are the work conditions favourable?

AREA	FACTORS	For me is there: YES/NO	For my staff is there: YES/NO
Reward	Money/Salary Pensions Perks Holidays/Time off Flexitime Car provided Travelling to work		
Office	Chair Desk Lighting Temperature Noise Decor Open plan/Private		
Equipment/ Resources	Readily available Up to date Good working order Secretarial Information resources		

How do your working conditions fare when set against the conditions mentioned here? Were there any factors to which your trigger words related? In the next chapter we will look at ways of adapting to or changing factors which are sources of frustration or stress. Changing minor sources of stress can greatly enhance the resources you have available for coping with more major stressful factors.

A client who attended a stress management course recently was no longer working with pressure but had become stressed. He was caught on the stress-spiral and could not see how to make some of the necessary major changes in his life. So he decided to start by building up his coping resources and change some of the minor sources of stress in his life.

He had always found the pale yellow colour of his office very dreary and it was now very tatty anyway. He asked for the office to be painted and some plants to be put in. He could not believe what a difference it made to his mood every morning when he went to work. Instead of a dreary dull room to work in, he had a bright, fresh environment to help him cope with the other demands of his day. He had made his work conditions more favourable.

Do you feel you have good working relationships?

FACTORS	Do you feel you are: YES/NO	Are my staff: YES/NO
In touch with boss		
Listened to		
Assertive enough		
Supported		
Understood		
Given praise		
Valued		
Able to manage your time well		
Equipped with a sense of humour		
Prepared for change		
Given healthy competition		
Suffering jealousy between departments		
Discriminated against: SEX AGE RACE		
Anxious		
Exploited		

Our relationships with other people depend very much on our own attitudes. Depending on who we are dealing with - so we change. We are different for different people: compare yourself at work talking to the boss, to the 'you' at home with the family.

Feelings and perceptions of relationships are particularly varied so if how you feel or perceive you feel is not included, add it to the list yourself. Using your trigger words examine how these feelings develop. This will give a useful insight into the kinds of relationship which will help you to make the most of pressure.

If '**success**' is a trigger word for you it's easy to see how being given praise and feeling valued will spur you on and you will continue to thrive. If you feel are **aren't** given praise or valued, you may well become despondent and uninterested and stress may be experienced.

These questions are also helpful in identifying how to motivate your staff. Work through this chapter with them and you will determine when they feel motivated and, therefore, how to continue to motivate them. Even though they will be aware that you know their motivational requirements, you'll be able to provide a lift just at the right time when they need it.

Women at work

As we proceed through the 1990s more women will enter into full-time employment as the size of the work population declines. Woman at work face a number of stressors as a result of their **sex**. Women in management positions which are not viewed as 'women's work', e.g. engineering, are particularly vulnerable. Women generally tend to have high expectations of themselves; they may experience promotion blocks, sexual harassment, child care difficulties, or conflicts between home and work. So far society has not caught up with the implications of women in the workforce and the inequalities which still exist.

As a manager it is important to be aware that particular problems may exist for women. If they do, then the attitudes and organisation of the workforce should be examined.

To sum up ...

Good working relationships promote effective communications and leave less room for ambiguity. We will see when looking at life-events how important all relationships are to our well-being. Often working relationships are the hardest to deal with as it seems easier to ignore feeling and emotions. So take time to consider how you feel about your relationships at work.

By answering the three questions on page 89 you have begun to consider some of the factors at work which may cause a pressure situation to become a stressful one. If you are stressed, you may have discovered some of the reasons why. But this is only half the story. Only one-third of our time is spent at work. Just as important are the changes and events which occur in our time at home.

Life–events and change

Although we have looked at the factors associated with work which may cause 'pressure' to become 'stress', it is often a major life-event or change which actually disrupts the balance. Recognising the significance that these changes or events may have on your life enables you to make the necessary compensations in other areas if they occur.

These are events which are unavoidable and will affect most of us at some time during our lives, for example, death, illness or injury to our family or friends. Other events may relate to work, financial difficulties or marital problems. Some require judgement or choices, such as whether to move house or change jobs.

On page 99 is a list of 'life-events' adapted from the work of two American physicians, Dr Holmes and Dr Rahe. They identified these from thousands of case histories as events which preceded illness. They then asked 400 people to analyse this list and assign numerical values to each event, dependent on the amount of adjustment people felt they would need to make.

It is interesting to note that of the ten top-scoring 'life-events', only one relates to work, and five out of the ten relate to marriage in some way. Relationships tend to be significant causes of stress, be they with your spouse, children, neighbour, boss or work colleagues. Therefore, do not underestimate the impact a difficult relationship may be having on your life. Consider how you are going to address that fact, rather than trying to hide the associated feelings somewhere.

The inclusion of seemingly pleasant and enjoyable experiences, such as the addition of a new family member, outstanding personal achievement or a holiday, illustrates how even favourable change places demands upon our coping resources.

Events in isolation may be distressing but we are likely to be able to cope with them. However, too many 'life-events' or changes in a short space of time will burden the coping resources, and illness is likely to result.

The Holmes-Rahe scale of 'life-events'[1]

EVENTS	VALUE
Death of spouse	100
Divorce	
Marital separation	
Imprisonment	
Death of close family member	
Personal injury or illness	
Marriage	
Dismissal from work	
Marital reconciliation	
Retirement	
Change in health of family member	
Pregnancy	
Sex difficulties	
Gain of new family member	
Business readjustment	
Change in financial state	
Change in number of arguments with spouse	
Major mortgage or loan	
Foreclosure of mortgage or loan	
Change in responsibilities at work	
Children leaving home	
Trouble with in-laws	
Outstanding personal achievement	
Partner begins or stops work	
Begin or end of school or college	
Change in living conditions	
Change of personal habits	
Trouble with boss	
Change in work hours or conditions	
Change in residence	
Change in schools or college	
Change in recreation	
Change in church activities	
Change in social activities	
Minor mortgage or loan	
Change in sleeping habits	
Change in number of family meetings	
Change in eating habits	
Holiday	
Christmas	
Minor violations of the law	

1. Holmes,T.H. and Rahe,R.H. 'The social readjustment scale' in *Journal of Psychosomatic Research 1969.*

■ Age and Life-events

Another way of analysing the predictable events of our lives is by association with age. The evolution of our lives follows a general pattern. There will be periods of stability and periods of ending previous patterns and beginning to move towards a new set of goals.

Awareness of these patterns gives us the opportunity to approach them equipped with adaptive resources.

It is useful for those in a managerial position to be aware of these changes. You are likely to be managing people older and younger than you and this greater insight may be appropriate in terms of their age.

Age and 'life-events'

AGE	EVENTS
Beginning adulthood (17 - 22)	Exploration (College exams) First job Responsibility Managing finance Emotional relationships Building confidence
Becoming an adult	Stability versus exploration Commitment to career Settle down - own home Values Goals Achievement/progress Question what they've established Financial management for self
Turning thirty	Transition More serious More restrictive Greater responsibility to partner/family Marital problems and divorce peak Change occupation
Late thirties	Stability Wants place in society Attaining career goals Effort to build better life Financial dependents
Mid-life	Transition Question achievement New discoveries False dreams/goals
Retirement	Stability or transition or exploration Self-esteem Health Career over New self-development Adjusting financially

Lifestyle

All these factors place strain on the coping resources of our body. If the alarm response is continually stimulated, we know what detrimental effects may be experienced.

There are other factors which can deplete the body's ability to copy in relation to one's lifestyle.

■ Chemical stimulants

The use of tobacco, alcohol, caffeine and other stimulating drugs have detrimental effects on the body. Although the user 'perceives' them to be of assistance, they are actually depleting available resources. The body becomes far more vulnerable to infection and disease.

■ Diet

The high-cholesterol levels associated with stress and the resultant risk of coronary heart disease will be increased when a diet containing rich, high-cholesterol foods is consumed. Somehow a stressful job always seems to go hand-in-glove with plenty of entertaining in expensive restaurants. The stressed restaurateurs are desperate to ensure you had a wonderful time and that you feel very spoilt, so plenty of rich ingredients are used. Even when you are not eating in expensive restaurants, it is often difficult to stick to a well-balanced diet. In the next section we will look at ways of combating this.

Another result of the alarm response is that blood is directed away from the gut, so nutrients are less well absorbed - further leading to malnutrition. A lack of vitamins, particularly vitamin C, leaves us open to infections and colds, and feeling tired.

■ Exercise

Because of our sedentary lifestyle exercise now has to be actively sought. Time has to be planned and it can often seem difficult to fit it in. But for good posture and to expend the stores of energy built up for physical activity, it is essential.

■ *Lack of sleep*

When the coping resources are being stretched, more sleep is needed to allow the body more time to recover. Of course, what happens is just the opposite. As you overextend yourself physically and mentally, less time seems to be available for sleep.

■ *Mental attitude*

If pressure has long since given way to stress and you are caught in various stress-spirals there is a sense in which your mental attitude contributes to your reactions and behaviour. If you have formed stress patterns and expect each day to be as bad as the one before, then often it will be.

Have you become resigned to the way you feel physically and the way you organise yourself? Do you feel it's hopeless because it's all to do with the organisation you work for and nothing to do with you? Are things out of your hands? Do you just do as you are told?

If the answer to these questions is 'Yes', then you have become resigned to your circumstances. One of the factors that needs addressing is your mental attitude. Hopefully, as you read this book you will feel that you do have the ability to begin the process of change.

If you have noticed this type of mental attitude in the people you work with, this may be one of the first things that has to change – believing there is a problem which can be solved!

A voyage of discovery

By now you should have identified factors in your work life, home life and lifestyle which are potential threats to you becoming stressed. You may feel that some factors are influencing you already and causing stress. Either way, it is by learning skills of awareness first, and then identifying the factors, that it is possible to determine how you are going to prevent or combat these factors.

This voyage of discovery about yourself is also going to enhance your ability to identify stress in others. However, their perception of life will be completely different to yours, so keep an open mind and don't pre-judge on the basis of your own personal experience.

Identifying stress in others

As you develop awareness of the existence of stress, its effects on health, behaviour and emotions and which factors are likely to cause 'stress', you will not only benefit yourself but become more adept at identifying stress in those around you. Below we have grouped the signs to look out for, since until you've identified the existence of stress you cannot begin to help someone.

■ *Physical signs*
- Weight change – loss
                    – gain
- Tense posture
- Trembling
- Increased smoking/cups of coffee
- Pallor/blushing
- Breathlessness
- Inarticulate in speech
- Sighing
- Colds or infections
- Nail-biting
- Tearful
- Frowning
- Body language
- Twitches, tics
- Tone of voice

■ *Behavioural and emotional signs*
- Late for work, long lunchbreaks
- Clock-watching
- Reduction in output
- Mistakes
- Poor memory
- Loss temper, mood swings, over-reaction
- Withdrawal socially
- Poor decision-making
- Forgetful
- Poor time-management
- Failure to meet deadlines

What to do

If you decide that someone is stressed, use your knowledge of that person and the existing circumstances to help you decide what to do. It is not advisable to approach them directly about their situation, as they will feel very threatened. If they are aware that they are stressed, they probably think they are doing a good job of disguising this to others.

Gain the trust of this individual; ensure that they feel you have an understanding relationship. (In the next section we will touch on counselling skills.) You may not be the right person to help them, but at least you could point them in the right direction. There are some useful addresses and telephone numbers at the back of this book.

Prevention is always better than cure, so having looked at some of the factors which may add to stress levels, aim to make appropriate changes. Provide an environment which is as pleasant as possible. Examine your attitude towards work. Long hours spent at work do not equate to working hard or efficiently. Instead, a great deal of unproductive time slips by, the quality of work suffers and an inefficient use of energy results. When somebody is spending long hours at work, ask yourself 'Why do they need to?' Could you help in some way? If it is a short-term behaviour pattern due to a deadline, encourage them to compensate afterwards with some relaxing time. Plan this time with them.

The extraordinary fact is that you will probably find it hard to find somebody who isn't stressed to some extent. This is useful in many ways because problems can then be approached together. There's nothing worse than feeling the odd one out. If one person does stand out from the rest, giving that person support now could mean that you receive support when you need it.

Section 4:
MAKING THE MOST OF PRESSURE

Checklist

☐ How do you decide whether to 'adapt' or 'change'?

☐ Do you know how to keep demands within your own capabilities?

☐ What skills and resources do **you** need to develop to make the most of pressure?

☐ Have you made a plan in order to make the most of pressure using a series of peaks and troughs?

Making the most of pressure

We have identified pressure as being a useful tool in improving performance and productivity as long as we are not over-exposed to it. Developing the skills to maintain a balance between perceived demands and the ability to cope, i.e. not allowing situations to escape beyond our control, is the primary objective of this section.

You are about to embark on the adventure of change to maximise your potential and enjoy the benefits of a healthy mind and body. You may need to make major changes or simple adaptations to your existing circumstances.

Some things are better approached directly and reduced or eliminated rather than trying to develop ways of coping with them more effectively. For example, drinking alcohol is not a beneficial way to achieve relaxation. It is likely to deplete your coping ability in the long term, so seek an alternative form of relaxation after work other than a trip to the pub on the way home. However, such a thing as your journey to work may be impossible to change, so look for ways of lessening its impact; travel at different times, listen to pre-recorded books on tape, see it as a useful time in your day to practise your awareness exercises.

Your trigger words will have helped you to identify those factors/qualities that will determine whether or not a situation will contain pressure and thus result in success, or threatening elements which may lead to stress. Now, by introducing change or adaptation to circumstance, we can ensure that we are operating under ideal conditions. We can maximise the effects of pressure as long as we know how to relax, rest and revitalise our bodies to meet the next challenge with just as much enthusiasm.

Not only will this be useful as far as personal needs are concerned, but also in managing the amount of pressure you create for a member of your team, and in knowing when to 'up the tempo' or slow it down.

When faced by a day that is jam-packed with appointments and tasks, what is going to determine how you view that day? Are you going to see it as an exciting challenge which will result in achievement and rewards, or will it seem daunting and give you the feeling that the day will slip by without the successful completion of any task? The way you perceive the day will be influenced by your personal attitude and the resources you have to deal with the situations.

By addressing those factors you have identified as potential threats to pressure becoming stress, ways of coping can be developed. There techniques may be regarded as 'stress-proofing'.

Not only are these techniques applicable to day-to-day events but also to the unforeseen life-events which we have discussed. Adaptation to these is less demanding where coping resources are available. It is necessary therefore to 'stockpile' and keep some in reserve.

A balance in our life between work, play, friends and family is essential if we are to make the most of pressure. We must plan our time in terms of peaks and troughs; peaks of pressure where energy is used with the 'adrenalin' flowing, compared with quieter times which are just as pleasurable but allow the body to revitalise. This is the spice of life, the light and the shade. Going flat out all the time is equally as dull as being understimulated.

In turn these 'peaks and troughs' must balance in all areas of your life. There will be peaks and troughs at work and home, in relationships with family and friends. Plan the peaks and troughs of your day, the week and the year. These will include some of the techniques you have learned already and some of the skills described in this section.

Checklist

☐ How are you going to decide between adaptation or change?

☐ Do you have enough resources available to change?

☐ Have you planned your change in the four stages?

☐ Can you establish the necessary motivation to adapt?

Adaptation or change

■ *Establishing resources for change*

We saw from the list of life-events on page 99 how the majority related to 'change' of some sort. At work, organisational change or technology have also been identified as stress factors. Change causes conflict and discomfort, the effects of which are frequently underestimated. Therefore, a change in your behaviour, outlook or circumstance is a potential factor of stress in itself.

How are you going to decide whether or not you are going to **adapt** to a factor and deal with it more effectively or obliterate a factor by **change**? For example, if you are not stimulated by your job or do not enjoy the rewards it affords you, then adapting by improving your time-management skills is not going to help you. Determining if you have the necessary resources to initiate a major change - in this case a new job – will help you decide how to approach this situation.

Having confronted yourself honestly, you may know that changing your job is the answer; but you may feel you do not have the necessary resources, e.g. finance, training, suitable alternative. Therefore, changing jobs at this stage might be stressful and therefore counter-productive. In this case, by adapting and increasing resources, for example by attending a training course which would provide stimulation and preparation for a change of job, you may ultimately be able to initiate your desired change.

Look at the list on the next page to help you to decide if you have the necessary resources available for a change. This may relate to minor changes as well as more major ones.

■ *Assessing availability of resources*

Motivation	Yes/No
Time	Yes/No
Confidence	Yes/No
Health	Yes/No
Money	Yes/No
Awareness	Yes/No
Education/information	Yes/No
Rest	Yes/No
Relaxation	Yes/No
Self-esteem	Yes/No
Creativity	Yes/No
Balanced diet	Yes/No
Emotional support	Yes/No
Positive thoughts	Yes/No
Balanced posture	Yes/No
No dependants	Yes/No

If your answer to the majority of the questions above is 'Yes' it suggests that you have the available resources to achieve a change. However, if the majority of your answers is 'No' then that suggests you are not quite ready to overcome a stress factor, and should build up your resources by changing or adapting the stress factors that you are able to.

▰ Planning change

In life there are three things we can count on: death, taxes and change! It is useful therefore to know how to approach change.

Think of change as a dynamic process which involves four stages:

* determining the change desired;
* planning;
* consideration;
* action and assessment.

This list is largely self-explanatory. The most crucial stage is consideration. This may involve consultation with your work colleagues, family or friends. At this stage you will establish the support which may be essential for the success of your plan. Often it will be a lack of communication at this point which leads to an unsuccessful outcome. An example can be seen in large organisations when change is implemented without those involved being encouraged to discuss the changes or being adequately prepared for them.

As managers, to implement change, consultation will:

* allay fears and prejudice;
* inform accurately;
* allow appropriate modifications;
* encourage the discussion of the benefits and new roles;
* obtain approval or acceptance.

▰ Adapting and motivation

If any change is instigated, there will be a new set of circumstances to which to adapt. For example, if you change jobs, you will have a new set of demands, colleagues and environment to adapt to, the difference being that this is your choice and, therefore, you are suitably motivated.

Adapting to existing circumstances that you cannot change often gets significantly harder simply because your motivation is not so great.

For example, when you are asked to stay late and cancel your dinner engagement, it's not the same as adapting to staying late when you want to complete some work before going on holiday at the weekend. In one situation you exercise choice; in the other it is imposed upon you.

It is useful to consider, therefore, that when when you adapting to a situation just as much thought and planning should take place. In addition, consider your motivating and supporting elements and don't lose sight of them. After attending time-management courses, clients felt they had learned useful techniques but within a couple of weeks had fallen back into old habits. The initial enthusiasm was not sufficiently motivating. This is not uncommon.

We suggest that one of the ways of overcoming this is to use the support of people at work and ensure that they wish to make changes or adaptations with you. We do not mean just those on the course with you but other colleagues from the boss to the secretaries and clerical staff. Decide what you believe are the benefits and go for them. Timetable a regular five to ten-minute slot each week to discuss 'how' this scheme is working and any modifications which need to be made.

Basically you follow the same four-stage process used for change:

- determine the adaptation desired;
- plan;
- consider/renew;
- action and assessment.

If the adaptation you are making is more personal, use the same principles to establish and maintain your motivation. You may still wish to discuss your plans and share successes with your colleagues.

Decide what are the benefits

Timetable a regular slot to assess your progress.

Enjoy the benefits and congratulate yourself on successfully adapting or changing.

Checklist

Do you know yourself?

☐ Do you respect yourself and hold yourself in esteem?

☐ Are you working in the right job to suit you?

☐ Can you say 'no'?

☐ Are you aggressive, assertive or passive in your responses?

☐ Do you say what you mean?

☐ Are you a perfectionist?

Do you have good organisational skills?

☐ Do you plan your time effectively?

☐ Are you good at setting goals and aims?

☐ Do you delegate and organise work for other people?

☐ Are you working effectively and efficiently?

☐ Do you ask for help when you need it?

How do you prepare for life events?

☐ Do you anticipate these?

☐ Can you avoid uncertainty?

Keeping demands within your capabilities

To continue to enjoy working under pressure, there are three main points to remember:

(1)   Demands upon you, perceived or otherwise, should remain within your capability, and you must know where your limits lie.

(2)   You must build up resources/skills to deal effectively with the demands you have chosen to accept.

(3)   Be aware of life-events, some arising out of the blue, that are likely to befall you and do not underestimate their impact upon your coping abilities. When you become stressed or if you are already stressed, these three points may not apply because it is difficult to know your limits, and the events feel imposed on you. You feel a victim of circumstances and are no longer a master of your own destiny.

■ *Knowing yourself*

As we have said, knowing yourself is a vital prerequisite to being able to manage pressure successfully. How else will you know how much you can take on? How else will you know whether a job is right for you? This all seems fairly self-evident.

As you have been practising awareness exercises, you will have already discovered things about yourself you didn't know. There is always room to know yourself better.

To make the most of pressure you need to be aware of the messages coming from your body, how tired or tense you feel. You must also be aware of how you react to situations, and ensure that you are objective and act in a rational and appropriate way.

■ *Self-image*

How does the image we have of ourselves, or our self-image, evolve? From a very early age we are brought up with expectations, e.g. owning a car, marriage, position in society. We are influenced by our parents' behaviour, standards, beliefs and reactions.

If we are constantly treated as intelligent, or beautiful, or weak-willed or stupid, eventually we will believe it. This may give us a distorted picture and leave us holding irrational beliefs about ourselves.

So how do we start to roll back the blinds and start looking at ourselves and our beliefs in a rational way? Remember that the difference between pressure and stress is in the way we perceive events. So spend some time looking at these beliefs or perceptions of yourself and see whether they match the reality.

Write down ten statements starting with: 'I am...'

Now discuss these with a trusted friend. You may be surprised how much more positively they view you. We are often fiercely judgemental and hard on ourselves. How does your perception of yourself and the reality of **you** as seen by your friend balance out?

Some of the items on your 'I am...' list may seem very rational - others irrational. Albert Ellis and Robert Harper introduced in their book *A Guide to Rational Living* a list of irrational beliefs. Some are directed at ourselves and begin with 'I' - others relate to other areas of our life and environment and how we can react.

■ Irrational beliefs directed at yourself

(1)   I need plenty of love and approval for many of the things I do.

(2)   I should be able to do everything well.

(3)   If something bad happens, I must worry about it.

(4)   By avoiding responsibility, I will enjoy life more.

(5)   Rather than risk failure, it is easier to avoid difficult things rather than try to accomplish them.

Irrational beliefs directed towards events around you

(1) It's terrible when things aren't going well in my life.

(2) If this goes wrong, I'm going to feel awful and there's nothing I can do about it.

(3) Some people are bad and should be punished.

(4) What I feel, what will happen to me now and in the future will be determined by what has happened to me in the past.

(5) There should be perfect solutions for everything.

Do you sometimes find yourself thinking like this?

Go through the list and tick the ones that apply to you.

Be careful of thinking or making statements that start with: 'I must...', 'I have to...', or 'I should...'. They are often related to irrational beliefs; so are words like awful, horrible and terrible. How often do you use words like these about yourself or someone close to you?

The next step, once you have caught yourself voicing these irrational beliefs, is to actively debate them. Why should I always...? Why can't I stand...?, etc. Try and do this every time you catch yourself using these irrational and very stress-producing thoughts. Don't be angry or upset with yourself if you miss opportunities to do this; just be pleased when you are actually able to carry it out.

Here is an example of how important it is to remove these irrational beliefs:

Mary worked for one of the partners of a local solicitors, firm. She was referred to us by her doctor as she was suffering from headaches, sore neck and shoulders. During the treatment sessions, we ascertained that her problems were made worse by stress at work. Her boss was very demanding, expecting a very high standard of the work that she typed and also dropping several urgent letters on her in the late afternoon. This invariably meant that she had to stay late in order to complete the work.

We discussed her problem and found that it was very important to her to gain her boss's approval of her work. She became aware that this was irrational and that this view was causing her to stay late and not complain about being given such unreasonable working practices. This insight was enough for her to enjoy satisfaction when she had completed her work to the best of her ability within the appropriate hours. She explained to her boss that she was employed to work until 5 o'clock and that if he gave her urgent letters late in the afternoon, she would be unable to leave at this time.

Right job, Right person

Using the three questions from the previous section:

- What does the job involve?
- Are the conditions favourable?
- Do you have good working relationships?

These questions are fundamental in deciding which job is for you. People often end up in the wrong job when they try to please someone else with the choice they make, such as their father or a spouse.

Internal promotions that do not involve a formal interview may also lead to a mismatch of job and employee. The employee is so overcome by flattery at being asked to do this new job that any structured consideration or analysis of the job description - if there is one - may well not be properly made. Over-promotion is also a common situation; it can lead to someone who usually looks good working with pressure being strained beyond his or her capabilities and showing signs of stress. Formal interview proceedings, in both situations, can ensure that both parties give appropriate consideration to potential promotion and so avoid unnecessary stress developing.

Taking control

Being assertive is about taking control, being honest with yourself, self-confident and rational. It does not necessarily mean getting your own way all the time, but when you're feeling balanced, it is easier to compromise.

When pressure is working well, you feel confident and remain objective; therefore, it is not difficult to be assertive, and to express your thoughts, wants and needs clearly.

When threatened by stress, assertiveness can often be lost and, with it, your control. Either the **passive** response of saying nothing, hiding your feelings or the **aggressive** response of losing control, becoming angry and having an outburst may be the result. Both are factors which add to stress and initiate the alarm response and the subsequent hormonal activity in the body. Tension builds up in the body and you will associate bad breathing patterns and posture with this type of behaviour. Although, in the short term by either suppressing how you felt, or getting it off your chest, you may feel you have coped, the truth is your self-esteem will be in decline.

The simplest of incidents can trigger these responses, such as giving a lift to someone who never has his own transport home. He's asked several times and you've agreed, not pointing out that it is out of the way (**passive**). Today, he asks again and you snap and growl at him, grumbling that he should get his transport sorted out - but still take him home (**aggressive**). He doesn't realise it is **him** that's making you cross and thinks you must have just had a bad day. The following day you decide to take an assertive course of action and simply say 'No' - you can't give him lifts anymore as it takes you too far out of your way (**assertive**). The situation is then resolved once and for all.

Assertive behaviour or responses require respect for oneself and other people. There are basic human rights to which everyone is entitled. Saying 'No' is one of those rights and yet it is seemingly one of the hardest responses to make. It is often seen as being unco-operative, or an admission that you can't cope, for instance, with any more work. People are afraid of being unpopular or losing their job.

This does not only apply in your working life but also in your domestic situations, relationships and involvement in organisations and clubs etc. How often have you heard yourself saying 'Yes' when you meant 'No'? Taking on too much and not knowing your capabilities, will result in your feeling hassled and rushed; your performance will suffer, more stress will develop, and this will lead to more poor decisions and the **stress-spiral**.

Practise saying 'No', just say it out loud or to yourself in the mirror. Instead of reacting to situations with excuses rather than being straightforward - say 'No' - if that's what you mean. You will be respected a great deal more in the long run.

What other rights can you uphold by being assertive? One is the right to make a mistake without humiliation or guilt. Everyone makes mistakes; on average two out of every ten decisions will be mistakes. You also have the right to change your mind, ask for help, state your needs and stand up for your rights.

But how do you achieve this without being aggressive? You may also be sensitive to how others will react to you. For a start, if you simply stated your mind, which you are entitled to do in a non-threatening way, and offence is taken, then that is not your problem but that of the person you're dealing with.

Tune into your body; become aware of how you are reacting to requests and situations. If you're making the most of pressure and are well balanced, no perceived threat should come to mind.

However, if you feel a frown on your face, a cramp developing in your stomach, your headache getting worse or muscle tension mounting - 'STOP'. Ground yourself with a few deep breaths.

'Relax and let go', let the muscle tension melt away, and now say what you feel.

You may wish to rehearse this with a friend or alone in front of a mirror. Imagine yourself saying how you feel and what your needs are, and then imagine the response of the person you are talking to. It may take a while to build your confidence sufficiently in this way. Ultimately, when the time is right and the opportunity avails itself, you will speak your mind.

Enjoy the boost to your self-esteem and confidence.

■ *Perfectionism*

People who are described as perfectionists are generally extremely demanding of themselves at work and elsewhere. They seek to better their best performance to date, but in so doing, waste a lot of time. Instead of simply accepting their best efforts, they will procrastinate in their search for perfection. The perfect is practically unattainable so why not settle for just 'best' or 'above average', enjoying those moments that are nearer to perfect.

It will be a lot easier to proceed with work and you'll be amazed at how much more you achieve and how much less exhausted you feel. You will no longer have the worry, apprehensions and fears that things aren't working out just as perfectly as you would like. You'll also be a much easier person to live and work with.

Organising, prioritising, delegating

■ Introduction

Time, the steady metronome, towers above us all. We all have opinions about time - sometimes it flies past, another time it drags. What is your opinion of time? Is there enough of it? In this section we will see how important it is to use this vital commodity! Whether we are rich or poor, we still have the same number of hours in a day. The right managing of time enables us to achieve goals, work effectively and keep breathing - just as long as we plan!

What would you do if a good fairy appeared on your shoulder and said 'I can give you an extra hour in your day'? How would you spend this extra hour? Perhaps it would be an extra hour with your children, reading a novel or playing tennis. Make a note of how you would use this time as it's the prize that good time-management will bring.

Time is a resource, its 'sell-by date' is **now** and it doesn't carry a money-back guarantee! Time can trickle through your fingers like sand. If I asked you how you had spent the last week, the chances are you wouldn't be able to give a detailed account. As a resource, it's rather like money – if you don't keep track of where your money goes, it is easy to find a large overdraft on your next bank statement. You can't go into the red with time, but if you don't use it effectively, then you will not progress to your goals as quickly as you would wish.

■ Setting your goals

Goals are the things you wish to achieve. They have to be realistic and achievable while being both challenging and interesting. They are one of the ways you balance your perceived demands against your coping skills or resources. Plenty of soul-searching and thinking is needed to work these out, but once you have, you can start to focus your resources on achieving these goals.

A certain amount of single-mindedness may be required to help you achieve these goals. Be a little more assertive, not aggressive; decrease the amount of interruptions. Or it may be that you need some help to plan your day more effectively. All of these will be discussed under the broad heading of time-management.

■ *Setting realistic goals*

If you keep motivated, enthusiastic and pressurised it means you are working well, but towards what? Towards your goals, but what are they?

This section helps you to identify them and decide whether or not they are realistic, to prioritise them and help give you a timetable to achieving them. Goals are statements about where you want to go.

Let's start by getting you to list your goals. They should include work, family, friends and **you**! Now rate them in order of importance - three ticks for important, one tick for trivial. The next stage is to ask yourself if they are realistic; are you capable of achieving them? Cross out the ones you feel you can't achieve.

You should now be left with a list of goals which are achievable. The last step is to fit these into a time-frame. How long before you can travel to Australia? How long before you are promoted to supervisor? Put these dates in your diary. There should be short-term and long-term goals to achieve. Don't forget the long-term ones. Remember a 'journey of a thousand miles begins with one step'.

The greatest thing about planning goals is that it provides a focus for how we spend our time and energy. If our time and energy is spent at work or at home not working towards our goals, then why are we using our precious time like this?

■ *Working towards our goals*

You are now at the stage when you should be clear about what your goals are. If you are given new work, make sure you are clear about what is expected of you. Then ask yourself if it is realistic. If it is not, then state this and negotiate. In that way you can keep heading towards goals even if they are new.

You arrive at your desk to find a whole string of messages and a bulging 'IN' tray. The temptation is to dive in at the deep end and start with the first job you see. However, momentary calm and planning are called for. Close your eyes, take ten slow deep breaths in and out and look again. Start by prioritising your calls and paperwork. Have three coloured highlighters - red for 'urgent', yellow for 'not quite so important' and green for 'OK to leave'. Now you need to organise some time to do this work.

Avoid interruptions if possible; these break concentration and throw the seeds of chaos into plans. If people do interrupt, then organise a time later in the day to see them for a stated period. You will be surprised how heavy crises are resolved, people will start taking more responsibility and you will only be interrupted for real emergencies.

Use your diary to write down deadlines, appointments and meetings. Colour-code these with your highlighters; it will stop you worrying about missing them.

■ Delegation

Delegating work can be an excellent way of making the best out of your possible resources. You can divert demands away from you, which may have pushed you into the stress zone, while making the person to whom you have delegated the task feel needed and part of the team.

However, delegation is a task in itself and you need to be very clear about the information and instructions you give, and what you expect to receive back. You must also choose someone with the appropriate skills and resources to complete the task.

It is often difficult to decide which jobs to delegate. Remember two things:

(1)   The 80/20 rate, simply put: 20 per cent of the tasks we do
       will give us 80 per cent of the rewards.

(2)   It is quite likely that this significant 20 per cent will be at the
       top of your priority list, so do these yourself and delegate the
       less important tasks on your list.

These are all externally good ways of helping you work more
effectively. However, you may feel a more fundamental approach is
necessary to look at how effective you are.

Time-management

Do you recognise any of these symptoms of poor time-management?

I have to work long, long hours.

I can't delegate, no one ever does as good a job as me.

I'm always working under tremendous pressure.

I get anxious and seem to spend many hours not producing any work.

It's the old story. If you want to use time more effectively, then you
have to start from knowing what you are doing now. So let's look at
how you are spending your day at the moment. The way to do this
is to create a personal log of how you spend your time.

Divide your day into fifteen-minute sections. Your diary should
look like the one on the next page.

Date:				
Time	Time spent	Interruptions (✔ ✗)	Time spent	Interruptions (✔ ✗)
7.00			9.15	
7.15			9.30	
7.30			9.45	
7.45			10.00	
8.00			10.15	
8.15			10.30	
8.30			10.45	
8.45			11.00	

The next step is to create between 10 and 15 headings under which to analyse your time. These could be: work of low importance (WLI); work of medium importance (WMI); work of high importance (WHI); passive relaxation (PR), e.g. meditation, exercise (EX), shopping (Shop), housework and preparing meals (HC), travelling to work (Com), telephone (TC1), meeting (Mtg), eating (Eat).

Under the interruptions column indicate with a ✔ if you were interrupted for yes, and with a ✗ if you were not.

Once you have done this, you are now able to take a time inventory of your life. We suggest that a minimum of a week is necessary. This may seem like a big commitment, but you will discover how you actually use your time and how you think you use it, and the benefits are enormous. Take each task and ask if by doing it you got near to your goals? Did you need to do the task at all? If the answer is 'YES', then did you do it at the right time?

Do you do smaller tasks to avoid major ones? Are you using the 80/20 rule? Have you any recreation scheduled in? Is this done after work is achieved?

Or do you do recreation before achieving any work? This often leads to feelings of guilt.

Doing this will enable you to plan your daily schedule much more effectively at work, and balance this with home and recreational activities.

Remember that there are an awful lot of lonely, successful people out there, so balance your time-plan to include your family and friends.

Life-events

Life-events and pressure seldom go together. We have still not found a suitable way of dealing with personal crises, especially death, in our civilised Western culture.

If you've experienced bereavement yourself, have you wondered how it would have felt just to sit wailing for a few days and then remaining officially in mourning for as long as you needed to? The Third World and Arab countries have a far more appropriate way of **expressing** grief. Why is it that here we want to keep it all to ourselves!

It is frighteningly common to come across people in our practice who are harbouring unexpressed grief two, three or even more years after the death of a relative or close friend. They often present physical problems; they are tense because they have been 'holding back' unexpressed emotions which should have been released.

Similar physical patterns are associated with unexpressed emotions arising from other major life-events. Divorce, sexual difficulties, moving house, shock and injury all take their toll when faced alone without emotional support.

These events seldom go together with pressure as commonly people are back at work all too quickly, not allowing themselves to re-balance after this major trauma. The chances are they will become stressed while trying to catch up, or will resume a normal life when they don't feel very normal.

Bosses and employers are all too keen for workers to return quickly, yet it is likely that this will be a false economy in the long term. The potential for this person to develop a stress-related illness is quite high. Provide support at work when it's necessary and dividends stand to be collected in the future.

If you experience a number of life-events and you have suitable coping resources available, you will probably be able to continue working in a pressure situation, e.g. moving house, changing jobs. But keep a check on the number of life-events that occur. You never know when unexpected events may turn up, so if you work to capacity all the time it leaves no scope for further demands on you and renders you vulnerable. Aim to keep a little in reserve.

Uncertainty

The uncertainty of the diagnosis for a patient is often a most worrying time. Somehow, once they know what they're dealing with, they can move forward in their thinking. So much time is spent worrying about uncertainty.

One of the ways of dealing with this is to gather as much information as possible. Your most pressing question may be answered out of this information and you can rest easy again. This also applies to job interviews and presentations. Collect as much information, prepare yourself, foresee the unexpected. This will calm any nerves and ensure you perform confidently.

Too many uncertainties in your life at one time may cause stress, e.g. moving house but not knowing where you're going to live, not having a job, financial concerns. Avoid unnecessary uncertainty, make a plan, stick to it and move on to the next phase of life equipped to enjoy it, not to worry about it.

If you feel you have been living a 'stressed' rather than 'pressurised' lifestyle and are secretly or openly concerned as to the physical effects that your body may already be experiencing, such as high blood pressure, high cholesterol levels, dizzy spells, an ulcer, etc, allay your fears and uncertainties by consulting your doctor or attending a screening clinic. This may also help establish the motivation to adapt or change your circumstances.

Skills and coping resources to make the most of pressure

Checklist

Relaxation:

- ☐ I have planned relaxation and awareness routines.
- ☐ I monitor my posture.
- ☐ My desk and chair are a comfortable height.
- ☐ I think of posture when I'm driving.
- ☐ I know where my muscle tension develops.

Lifestyle:

- ☐ I always eat breakfast.
- ☐ I respect food and mealtimes.
- ☐ I stop eating when I'm full.
- ☐ I am selective in ordering food when I'm out.
- ☐ I eat a balanced diet.
- ☐ I drink 1 litre of water per day.
- ☐ I have a regular exercise routine.
- ☐ I enjoy the benefits of exercise.
- ☐ I understand the detrimental effects of smoking.
- ☐ I know how many units of alcohol I drink per week.
- ☐ I get plenty of rest, particularly after larger demands are placed on me.
- ☐ I could seek help from my doctor or complementary medicine.

Behaviour:

- ☐ I am less aggressive.
- ☐ I listen more to people.
- ☐ I try to see the other point of view.
- ☐ I think positively.
- ☐ I have a good sense of humour.
- ☐ I know where I belong.
- ☐ I have plenty of support networks.
- ☐ I discuss my sexual difficulties with my partner.
- ☐ I feel loved.

Stock-piling coping resources to make the most of pressure

Maintaining the flexibility to cope with the unexpected demands of the day will help you to keep up a situation of pressure rather than stress. If you have coping resources in reserve, you will be able to absorb the changes and demands placed on you. If, however, you are operating at full stretch with nothing in reserve, you will be too near your point of threshold and your balance may easily give way to stress.

Some ways of building coping resources have already been discussed, such as awareness, breathing, relaxation and posture. Other aspects in your life such as attitude, behaviour and lifestyle can also be modified to build coping resources.

■ *Awareness, breathing, relaxation and posture*

The 'skills' of awareness, breathing, relaxation and posture have already been discussed in terms of reuniting the mind and body. The aim of this is to develop a quietening of the mind and to begin assessing those areas in your life which make pressure effective for you and those areas which threatened it. While you developed those techniques, you were also building coping resources as you rebalanced the body and reopened the lines of communication between mind and body.

As you become more aware, on a day-to-day and then minute-to-minute basis of how you are responding to stimuli mentally and physically, so you can counter-balance any negative or debilitating effects quickly. You will not suffer fatigue and will remain alert to make good decisions and organise, prioritise and implement your plans efficiently. Use your relaxation skills to recharge your batteries, both during and at the end of the day.

Lifestyle

There are a number of ways in which you can alter your lifestyle to establish healthier habits and a fitter you. This builds up your resistance to stress. You will also have a high regard for yourself, feel more confident and less angry and irritable.

Diet, exercise, alcohol and caffeine consumption, sleep and rest are probably areas you know you could improve upon, areas which your mother told you about or you've heard about through the media. Perhaps because your mother told you or just because it seems too difficult to change, you still carry on doing the things that are bad for you and ignoring the things that are good for you!

In this section we have tried to present ideas in ways that will help you to change your habits while fitting into your regular pattern of life quite easily.

■ Diet

People generally have an idea of what is meant by a 'balanced diet':

- proteins;
- fats;
- carbohydrates;
- vitamins and minerals;
- low fat, low salt;
- high fibre;
- plenty of water;

or translated into:

- protein sources - meat, eggs and pulses or other;
- milk and cheese;
- cereals and breads;
- fruit and vegetables.

But what does that list mean in terms of what you eat for breakfast, lunch or supper, or when you eat, how you eat and what to choose when you're eating out?

Information bombards us; what's good for you one minute seems to be going to cause disease the next. It does seem confusing at times. Eating something in moderation from each group each day will provide a balanced diet.

Breakfast is often the least popular meal of the day yet it is the most important and should never be missed. It is often easy to skip it and just have a cup of tea or coffee; but without breakfast, you are likely to become tired during the morning, irritable and unable to concentrate as your blood sugar drops. Ideally, breakfast should contain foods which are slowly metabolised to sustain you through the morning, such as unrefined carbohydrates like those found in wholegrain cereals, protein and some fat. Porridge is a good cereal, or low-fat cheese and wholegrain bread. Lunch should then be a top-up meal and evening a light meal.

It is not necessary to stick to 'three square meals a day'. Eat when you are hungry. You may find you are able to miss lunch quite easily. If you do need lunch, don't eat it on the move. Stop what you are doing, relax, become aware that you are eating. You know from the alarm response that when stressed, blood is shunted from the digestive system to the muscles and heart to prepare the body for 'fight or flight'. When this happens, food is poorly digested and indigestion and stomach cramps are likely to result. Food needs to be given time to digest. If you know you're going to be busy, don't eat large meals which you haven't the time to digest properly.

In the evening, choose a light meal and eat as early as possible to give your digestive system maximum rest overnight. Eating late at night can make you feel tired and lethargic in the morning.

We've seen how stress causes the release of cholesterol and other fats into the bloodstream, and how high levels of circulating fats are associated with heart disease. It is thought to be a good idea to avoid fatty foods. By eating more fibre you help to reduce blood fats as the fats stick to the fibre, which is then flushed out of the system, and reduces the amount absorbed.

An adequate intake of vitamins helps combat infection (vitamin C) and aids mental activity and many chemical processes of the body (vitamin B complex). Citrus fruits, tomatoes, and green vegetables that are lightly cooked are rich in vitamin C and meats, yeast and wholegrain cereals are good sources of vitamin B complex.

Business people often have to eat out, so develop good habits when choosing foods. Avoid rich courses with cream and spirits, choose light dishes with fish and chicken and freshly cooked vegetables, steamed if possible. Instead of choosing three or four courses, limit yourself to two. When you feel full, stop eating. Don't finish what's on your plate just because it's delicious. You will enjoy your meal more if you don't suffer indigestion afterwards. Drink water instead of wine and choose herbal teas instead of strong coffee afterwards. Use your diaphragmatic breathing to help digest your meal. When you return to work you will find you are much more alert for the rest of the day.

Always try to eat your food slowly; digestion begins in your mouth as you chew your food. Savour the flavour! You will then find you are satisfied by less.

Drinking plenty of water is essential for good digestion, and for preventing constipation and dehydration. Aim to drink at least a litre each day. If you don't like tap water, there are excellent water filters available in jug form or as a unit attached to a normal sink.

A little consideration and rearrangement of your eating habits will add to your vitality and energy, giving you more coping ability for the demands of your life.

■ *Exercise has so many benefits*
Like it or not, due to man's ingenuity in devising many labour-saving devices, we now have to actively seek exercise. The bonus is that exercise has now become a recreational event! If you lack motivation, look at the list of benefits on the next page.

Exercise:

- relaxes tense muscles after a busy day;
- tones up flabby muscle and improves self-image;
- enhances sex life;
- helps fight off infection;
- improves endurance, so we react more slowly to stressful stimuli;
- improves co-ordination and body awareness;
- clears the mind and enhances mental agility;
- helps to reduce weight;
- reduces risk of cardio-vascular disease by reducing blood fats and high blood pressure.

Convinced?

How much exercise do you need?

After many exercise fads and crazes, a fairly consistent frequency and duration of exercise has been established.

Recommended minimum of three times spread through the week for between twenty and thirty minutes.

If you feel you haven't enough time, refer to the time-management section - don't use it as an excuse.

If you don't know how to begin - seek help.

There are plenty of clubs and facilities with properly trained staff to design an exercise programme to suit your needs. This will give you support and encouragement.

Choose an activity you enjoy. Begin with a colleague or friend and attend together. If you feel embarrassed about your shape or lack of fitness, don't let it stop you. Soon you will be feeling and looking good.

Always do some simple stretches before exercise to encourage the blood supply and circulation in your muscles. This plus eight to ten minutes 'cooling down'; i.e. stretching, keeping on the move walking, will all help prevent stiffness and injury. Remember to rehydrate yourself after exercise.

■ *Some tips to increase physical activity in your day*

- Use the stairs when you can, or share your ascent with the lift and the stairs!
- Get off the tube or bus a couple of stops before you need to and walk the rest of the way.
- Walk rather than drive if you can.
- Cycle when possible.
- Park your car and walk some of the way to the office.
- Keep your sportswear or swimsuit with you at work.
- Take a walk round the block in your lunch break.

■ *The poisons*

You want to make the most out of pressure so be environmentally friendly to your body. Caffeine, smoking, excessive alcohol and drugs are out. They severely deplete your body's coping resources. **Caffeine** is found in coffee, tea, and chocolate. It stimulates the nervous system and production of adrenalin, the harmful effects of which are associated with stress. The increase in heart-rate and stimulation of acid production in the stomach caused by caffeine can lead to irregular heartbeats, palpitations and heartburn, indigestion and aggravation of ulcers. So cut down on coffee and tea and replace them with water and herbal teas.

Excessive alcohol consumption leads to physical and behavioural problems. The recommended weekly intake for men is 21 units and for women 14 units, which should be spread throughout the week and not consumed in several heavy sessions.

$$1 \text{ unit } = \begin{array}{l} \textbf{1 spirit measure} \\ \textbf{1 glass wine} \\ \textbf{$\frac{1}{2}$ pint beer} \end{array}$$

Alcohol affects the heart and blood vessels and can lead to high blood pressure and abnormal heart rhythms. Damage to the liver is also associated with excessive alcohol. The high calorific level of alcohol can lead to weight problems and poor nutrition.

The effects on behaviour include disturbed sleep patterns, irritability, loss of mental alertness, poor relationships and loss of self-esteem.

In moderation, enjoy your tipple but look out for the soft drinks on the shelf. Fortunately there are many to choose from. Just because you start with a gin and tonic at the beginning of the evening, don't feel you have to stick with it. Go for just the tonic or choose mineral water instead. Avoid using alcohol as a form of relaxation. Use other techniques to unwind.

Smoking and **drugs** have extremely harmful effects on the body. Smoking has been clearly cited as a predisposing factor to lung cancer, heart disease and circulatory problems. Tobacco and drugs are often used as ways of coping with stress, although they ultimately compound it by reducing coping ability. These habits are difficult to break, but the detrimental effects are such that concerted effort should be made to 'kick the habit'. Seek help. Acupuncture and hypnotherapy can produce excellent results towards helping people give up. Useful addresses are included at the end of this book.

■ *Sleep and rest*
Ensure that you have adequate amounts of sleep and rest. Incorporate these in your 'peaks and troughs' planning. A common stress-spiral occurs when you work long hours in preparation for a major deal. Sleep time is reduced and tends to be disturbed by the high levels of arousal. If this happens, ensure you compensate by catching up on sleep once you have completed the peak in your work demands. Don't be swept along on to the next project until you have recovered fully. When life-events occur close together or are very significant, make a conscious effort to have more rest and sleep. Emotions are very draining and you need to recuperate if you experience emotionally traumatic events. Restore the balance.

Practise relaxation and meditation exercises to help you sleep. Exercise also helps relieve tension and aids restful sleep.

■ *Your doctor and complementary medicine*
Because of the increasing number of days lost from work due to stress-related illness and back pain, doctors are well aware of the significance of stress. They may offer health screening as a service within their practice to help you establish any physical effects of stress. Many are adopting a more holistic approach and will try to establish the reasons behind the symptoms, which enables them to advise on suitable relaxation or forms of complementary medicine which may be of benefit. It is always worth having a chat with your GP to help determine who could help you best. Useful addresses are included at the end of this book.

■ *Behaviour under pressure*
When you are being effective under pressure you will be calm, sensitive, talk clearly and apply yourself to the task in hand and remain patient. If you become stressed, have you noticed how it's easy to get angry, become irritable, aggressive and impatient? None of these reactions actually helps your situation; instead they impair your senses and judgement and you are more likely to make mistakes.

If you practise awareness and monitor the tension in your body it will provide warning signals for this type of behaviour. Identify ways of altering certain habits that are aggressive and impatient, and discipline yourself to act more serenely and calmly. On the next page you will find some tips for how to do this.

- talk slowly;
- smile;
- wait patiently - practise your relaxation and awareness techniques;
- linger over dinner;
- drive more slowly, overtake less;
- listen to somebody else;
- take a stroll;
- relax your shoulders and neck;
- notice life and nature around you;
- accept the things you cannot change;
- mistakes happen, don't dwell on them, move on and make the necessary compensations;
- don't overburden yourself with work and commitments.

■ *Being a good listener*

As a manager, listen to what people are saying, and enlist their help and support rather than abruptly ordering them about. Show some understanding even if you can't provide a solution. At least they will feel that somebody has 'heard' them and knows about their predicament. When someone approaches you with a problem, try to remain objective. Refrain from over-involvement to protect yourself from becoming stressed. Instead:

- ask open questions, use why, what, when and how;
- repeat the last phrase they have spoken if their flow is interrupted;
- define the time you have available and stick to it;
- don't be directive, help the person clarify the problem for themselves;
- recognise when the problem needs expert help and suggest a suitable person.

■ *Thinking positively*

It is easy to become negative when overwhelmed by stress. The power of positive thinking is immense however. Believe in your own coping abilities as you move towards a more balanced approach to life. Any hardship or difficulty you have to overcome should be a learning experience. Become interested in how you may progress through this difficult period, and determine the outcome. Visualisation techniques are very helpful.

Imagine in your mind the desired outcome of a situation. Picture yourself in that situation enjoying the benefits of a successful outcome. Rehearse it in your mind. Chase away any negative thoughts.

Be realistic in your criticisms, belief and aims. Don't always expect the best or the worst, but take it as it comes. It will be far less stressful and more enjoyable that way.

When confronted by a problem or having identified a factor which is a potential source of stress, the technique of 'brainstorming' is often useful in problem-solving. Having identified your factor, simply write down a list of all the possible solutions, no matter how crazy they may seem. When all possibilities have been expressed, analyse them and select those that are most likely to work. Visualise the outcome you desire with this course of action. By thinking positively, you are halfway there!

■ *Develop a sense of humour*

Laughter has been shown to raise the level of endorphins - the body's own natural pain-killers which create a sense of well-being. We often lose sight of the funny side of life when we are experiencing stress. Try not to let things get out of perspective; see the funny side of situations even though it may initially seem like a crisis. If you don't feel that work is the appropriate place for this, share the humour with your partner or a friend.

Sharing a joke at work is extremely enhancing in relationships. There is an air of respect around when people can enjoy a laugh with the boss. It makes you more approachable - you'll hear about problems soon. So don't miss that opportunity.

■ *A sense of belonging and support*

We all need to feel we belong, that we have a place in society, a home and a place to retreat to and enjoy, that we have a contribution to make. Acknowledgement and praise reinforce this sense. Encouraging self-esteem in others can boost their morale very effectively and will spur them on to further successes. Enjoy their achievements with them.

Support may come from family, friends or work colleagues. When working with pressure in our lives, we want support, not hindrance or obstacles from our relationships. A problem shared or discussed can be an effective way of beginning to deal with it.

■ *Love and sex*

From the cradle to the grave, we all need to feel loved. Yet when we become stressed and our mood and behaviour changes, we risk hurting the very people we love, and sometimes believe we ourselves are not loved. When was the last time you told your partner you loved him or her? You need to be reminded that you are loved every day. It can often be taken for granted, but it's somehow easy to forget.

Cuddling and stroking have been shown to be very therapeutic in lowering blood pressure and exerting a calming effect and are a very good way of relaxing.

As we have seen, libido is often lowered when we become stressed. Impotence, premature ejaculation and difficulty in reaching orgasm are all common problems that occur. This leads to a loss of confidence in sexual performance, and tension develops in the relationship. Talk about it, don't ignore it or pretend it's not happening, and it might resolve itself. Gain understanding of one another; how is it making you both feel?

Caressing and stroking can be very relaxing and a help before love-making. If you're experiencing problems, you can still kiss and cuddle, expressing love without necessarily having sex.

Sensual stroking and touching in areas you wouldn't normally touch yourself are great for increasing body awareness. Explore each other's body, find out where the most sensitive areas are. Bring yourself into the present, clear your mind of everything else, be aware of the pleasurable sensation of your body contact, flesh on flesh. Imagine how your touch is making your partner feel.

These are all ways of focusing your attention and building confidence. Make love without having sex - a lot less demanding on performance!

Developing a strategy in terms of peaks and troughs

You've now accumulated considerable amounts of information about pressure and stress. As you have been reading, you've probably picked out various points that apply to you. But what are you going to do now? How are you going to use this information? Use this image to balance your day, your week and the forthcoming year.

■ *Your day*

In time-management we looked at prioritising your day and planning your use of time. The most important commitments or work demands represent the peaks to your day when extra concentration and effort will be used. When you have completed these, it is important to re-balance. The extra demands on your concentration may inhibit your sense of awareness, so timetable a five-minute relaxation or meditation before beginning your next task. You will consequently approach this new task with more enthusiasm and energy. If an unexpected frustration or annoyance occurs, breathe deeply, let it flow over you, choose not to over-react. When you feel balanced, this is less likely to happen anyway.

■ *Your week*

This will include other forms of relaxing and revitalising. You may plan when you are going to include exercise, a special evening at home with the family, or an early night if you know you'll be having a long day. Including extra sleep-time is particularly important if it's going to be a busy week. Review your work at the end of each week. How balanced and grounded have you been? What would you like to change for next week? Your plans will have to be continually reviewed but don't lose your valuable troughs. Too many peaks will only result in pressure becoming stress and at that stage there are no peaks.

■ *Your year*

There are some times of the year that you know are likely to be particularly busy due to demand or staff holidays for example. If you know that a couple of months of the year will be like this, plan and book your holiday well in advance to follow this period. Psychologically, a well-planned holidaytime encourages you to pace yourself. You can work towards that holidaytime, by winding up commitments in the weeks preceding. Book new appointments or meetings for your return. There doesn't have to be a mad panic before you go so that it hardly seems worth the effort of going. Every six months plan your holiday or long weekends for the following nine months. Aim to space them evenly and work around them. If they have to be changed, don't simply miss them out - rebook!

Balancing demand with coping resources in this way will enable you to maximise the effects of pressure and to steer clear of stress.

■ *It sounds so easy*

It does sound easy when you read and plan, but the reality can work out differently. The great bonus is that you've already started by reading this book. A change of habits takes time, so don't become despondent if it doesn't happen overnight.

Courses and Consultancy

Paul Stamp and **Helen Froggatt** run workshops and seminars throughout the country. They offer 'made-to-measure' courses for companies and businesses. *Dolphin Stress Management*, 19 College Green, Gloucester GL1 2LR Tel: 0452-301748

Some Useful Addresses

Alcoholics Anonymous
PO Box 514
11 Redcliffe Gardens, SW10 9BQ
Telephone 071-352-9779

BACUP (British Association of Cancer United Patients, Their Families and Friends)
121/123 Charterhouse Street
London EC1M 6AH
Telephone: 071-608-1785
Cancer Info: 071-608-1661

British Association for Counselling
37a Sheep Street
Rugby, Warwicks, CV21 3BX
Telephone: 0788-78328

British Chiropractic Association Information Services
5 First Avenue
Chelmsford, Essex CM1 1RX
Telephone: 0245-358487

British Homoeopathic Association
27a Devonshire Street
London W1N 1RJ
Telephone: 071-935-2163

Divorce Conciliation and Advisory Service
38 Ebury Street
London SW1W 0LU
Telephone: 071-730-2422

Gamblers Anonymous
17/23 Blantyre Street
London SW10
Telephone: 071-352-3060

General Council & Register of Osteopaths
56 London Street
Reading, Berks RG1 4SQ
Telephone: 0734-576585

Stress Foundation
Cedar House
Yalding, Kent ME18 6JD
Telephone: 0622 814431

Women's Health Information Centre
52 Featherstone Street
London EC1Y 8RJ
Telephone: 071-251-6580

Yoga for Health Foundation
Ickwell Park
Northill
Biggleswade, Beds SG18 9EF
Telephone: 076-727 271/604/735